W9-AXU-291

EARTH
The Stuff of Life

EARTH

The Stuff of Life

FIRMAN E. BEAR

NORMAN : UNIVERSITY OF OKLAHOMA PRESS

BY FIRMAN E. BEAR

Theory and Practice in Use of Fertilizers (New York, 1938)
Soils and Fertilizers (New York, 1953)
(Ed.) *Chemistry of the Soil* (New York, 1955)
Earth: The Stuff of Life (Norman, 1961)

Library of Congress Catalog Card Number: 62-10763

Publishing Division of the University.
Manufactured in the U.S.A.
First edition, January, 1962.
Second printing, by offset, November, 1962.

This book is affectionately dedicated to

HELEN JUDY BEAR

who has overlooked my many fancies, foibles, and faults for fifty years of our married life. To her I owe a great debt of gratitude.

CONTENTS

The Earth is the Lord's and the fulness thereof; the world and they that dwell therein.

—PSALMS

PREFACE

THE stuff referred to in the title of this book is the inanimate matter of which Earth is made and out of which all living things that grow in such great variety and abundance are constructed. The starting point is the spark of life. Around such sparks of life plants build their substances. And from among these substances animals and men must choose their food.

The quantity and quality of the vegetation that grows in any given region depend largely on the nature of the soil and climate of that region. But they depend also on the kinds of plants with which the region is endowed, whether they be those arising from the evolutionary processes of nature or those resulting from supplemental breeding and selection by man.

The lithosphere, the atmosphere, and the hydrosphere are involved in the making of the soil that forms a mantle over the surface of Earth. In this soil live the myriads of microbes, out of it grow the many kinds of plants, and on it and on the plants it produces, man places his dependence for food and fiber.

This book is concerned with these matters, with particular reference to the United States of America. It goes into scientific detail only so far as seems essential for an understanding of the principles that are being dealt with. It is in no sense a comprehensive treatise on soils in relation to plant growth.

The primary purpose of the book is to bring the beneficence of nature into focus, as it was when man took over, as it is now, and as it could be if nature were more fully understood and aided by man.

No attempt has been made to give credit to the many men, both scientific and practical, to whom the author is greatly indebted for facts, principles, concepts, and philosophies. But none of these people should be held responsible for any errors in fact or interpretation that may have crept into this account of Earth and what grows upon it.

The author is particularly indebted to Miss Ethel L. Reed, who has typed and retyped the manuscript, meanwhile making many suggestions toward its improvement.

FIRMAN E. BEAR

New Brunswick, New Jersey
January 29, 1962

EARTH
The Stuff of Life

The soil is the one indestructible immutable asset that the nation possesses. It is the one resource that cannot be exhausted, that cannot be used up.

—MILTON WHITNEY

Chapter One

THE SOIL BENEATH OUR FEET

SOIL, like faith, is the substance of things hoped for, the evidence of things not seen. It is the starting point for all the living things that inhabit the earth. The flowers, fruits, and vegetables that grow in the garden, the trees that tower in the woods and forests, and the grains and grasses that flourish in the fields, as well as the animals that consume them—all owe their existence to the soil. And man himself, by way of the food he eats, is a product of the soil, and to the soil his body will be returned.

All the plants that grow out of the soil, including not only those with which we are quite familiar but thousands of other species as well, extend their roots farther and farther down into the soil as their tops grow higher and higher above it. They feed on the soil. Some idea of the extent of their feeding can be obtained from the quantities of ashes that remain when plants have been consumed by fire. These ashes are the soil part of plants. Even though ashes constitute only about 5 per cent of their oven-dry weight, plants could not survive without the soil-derived mineral elements of these ashes.

Likewise, the animals that feed on plants need not only the proteins, carbohydrates, and oils of which plants are mostly composed and which they manufacture out of air and water but the ash elements these plants take out of the soil as well. The bones of animals are made up mostly of substances obtained from the soil, their most important constituents being calcium and phosphorus, joined together with a trace of fluorine, as phosphate of lime. And every vital organ in the bodies of animals and man must contain its quota, not only of calcium and phosphorus but of all the other essential mineral nutrients that come from the soil by way of the plant, if it is to do the work for which it was designed.

The seemingly lifeless soil on which we trod is alive with an intricately organized society of countless billions of living things, each group of which has a specific piece of work to do. Mingling with these microscopic plants and animals are many larger forms of life, such as earthworms, nematodes, termites, and ants—all very busy with their peculiar undertakings.

Most insects harbor in the soil at some stage of their life histories. Moles, ground hogs, prairie dogs, and shrews make the soil their home. And lying dormant among these many very active forms of life are the living seeds of higher plants. Theirs is a highly precarious existence. They may be eaten by mice or attacked by fungi, such as the common molds. They may die from lack of oxygen when the soil becomes saturated with water and remains so for too long a period of time. Or they may germinate and start to grow, only to starve from lack of water or to be choked out by dense populations of weeds or other competing plants.

If a plant survives beyond infancy, it is still subject to various disasters, including being consumed by larger animals or harvested by man. In nature, however, enough seed of any given species of wild annual plant spring to full life each year, grow to be mature plants, and produce new seed that the perpetuation of the species is assured. Having accomplished its purpose, the mature plant eventually dies and falls back on the soil to become, in part, a portion of the soil.

A similar type of life cycle takes place with perennial plants, such as grasses, shrubs, and trees. They may lose a part of their produce to the soil each year, as in the dropping of the leaves of such deciduous trees as the oak and maple every autumn. But they renew their growth each succeeding spring, sometimes living a century or more. Yet even the tallest tree eventually falls to the ground to be gradually reduced by microbial processes to the substances out of which it was originally constructed. And among these substances are the soil-derived mineral elements. Although, in the slow-burning microbial processes, no ashes as such are seen, the soil-derived mineral elements in a tree or any other type of plant are returned to the soil in much the same form as a result of microbial action as they would have been if the tree or plant had been destroyed by fire.

What is soil? In largest part, soil is what is left of the rocks that originally covered the face of the earth after the winds and rains and the heat and cold of the centuries had broken them to pieces, and the water that fell as rain had dissolved out the most soluble portions and carried them away, largely out to sea.

But soil is more than a residue of rocks. It contains the remains of many generations of plants and animals that have lived on the earth. On and within the soil are the myriads of living things that use the soil as their abode. These are a part of the soil. And they subsist on both the mineral and the organic matter portions of the soil. Soil is a dynamic living entity that continues to change with time and circumstances.

Soil can be thought of in terms of its capacity to produce the plants one wants to grow, to form a firm foundation for a highway, or to construct a dam to hold in storage a city's supply of water. But soil can also be studied without reference to any of the many important uses to which it can be put. Considered as an entity in itself, the soil has certain readily apparent features, such as its color, the sizes, shapes, and arrangements of its component particles, and its internal air and water relationships. Its microbial population can be isolated and observed under a high-power microscope. The larger forms of animal life can readily be separated from the soil, or they may even be studied in place.

Colors of soils vary from the deep reds of the tropics, the yellow-reds of the semitropical regions, and the gray-browns of the warmer portions of the humid temperate zones to the grays of the cooler, moister regions farther north. Going from the more humid to the drier temperate climates, the gray-brown soils of the once forested areas are displaced by the black-brown soils of the prairies and plains, the chestnut brown soils of the semiarid regions, and the gray-red soils of the deserts. Under conditions of poor drainage, as in a wet subsoil or under a manure heap, blue-green and mottled colors will be noted. Along the seashore the white sands are found in abundance.

The sizes of soil particles vary from coarse sands, the grains of which are readily apparent to the eye, to the very fine clays that, when broken down into their individual units, can be seen only with a microscope. In between are the fine sands and the intermediate-sized silt particles. Every soil is made up of particles of a wide range of sizes. One or another of these sizes may predominate in any given soil, but most soils contain particles of all sizes between the coarsest sands and the finest clays. Large percentages of sand give soils a gritty feel, large percentages of silt give them a floury feel, and large percentages of clay make them sticky when wet.

Millions of the smallest particles of soil are often joined together to form much larger units. The cementing materials consist of sticky clay or gelatinous products that are formed during the rotting of soil organic matter. When these cementing materials are dried, whether by dry winds, the heat of the sun, the action of plant roots, or the freezing process, they shrink, drawing the particles surrounded by them into tight aggregates or granules. And once the gelatinous binding materials have been thoroughly dried out, they do not readily reabsorb moisture. Consequently, the granules may retain their sizes and shapes for a considerable period of time. Their formation and re-formation is essential in keeping soils, notably those with a high clay content, in good working condition, a state known as "good tilth."

The microbial population of the soil consists mostly of microscopic plants, particularly bacteria and fungi. Such animal forms as protozoa and nematodes also constitute important parts of it. Most of the several groups of microscopic plants live in co-operative association with each other, but some of them are parasitic. The microscopic animal forms are predatory, the protozoa, for example, feeding on the bacteria and fungi, and increasing or decreasing in number in proportion as the number of microscopic plants at their disposal rises or falls.

Some of the insects that spend a part of their lives in the soil use it merely as a place in which to harbor during dormant periods. Some of them, such as grubworms, the larvae of the June beetle, feed on the roots of plants growing on the soil. Earthworms are permanent residents of the soil, feeding primarily on dead organic matter in and on the soil. Many larger forms of animal life, such as prairie dogs and ground hogs, use the soil as a home but feed on the aboveground portions of plants.

Excretions and dead bodies of these various forms of plant and animal life provide food for the lower categories of the soil microflora. The dead body of a protozoon, a relatively large animal form in comparison to the plant-form bacterium, makes a choice morsel of food for the scavenging microbes. That of an earthworm provides a big meal for millions of these microbes. And when a large animal or plant dies and falls to the ground to become a part of the soil, very rapid multiplication of the scavenger microbes occurs with the result that it is quickly reduced to the atmospheric and soil constituents that went into its making.

The vegetation growing on any given area of soil in its virgin state provides a clue not only to the nature of the climate but to the nature of the underlying soil as well. The climate may vary all the way from that of the desert to that of the tropical jungles. And the vegetation, likewise, may vary all the way from the cactus of the arid regions and the short grasses and mesquite of the semiarid regions to the tall trees of the high-rainfall regions, with the tall grasses and shrubs in between.

This means that soil must be considered in relation to its environment. Soil, climate, and vegetation are so closely identified with each other that if one knows the facts about any two of these he can deduce most of the facts about the third. In other words, if one knows the nature of the soil and climate, he can predict quite accurately the nature of the natural vegetation. If he knows the nature of the soil and the vegetation, he can predict the nature of the climate. And if he knows the nature of the climate and vegetation, he can predict the nature of the soil.

If the climates and the associated plants that existed during the long period required for soils to develop and mature in widely scattered areas of the earth were essentially the same, this is reflected in the similarity of the soils in these areas. And this applies no matter what the nature of the rock from which the soils were formed. That is not to say that the soils will be identical either in their physical or chemical makeup, but they will bear a very strong over-all resemblance to each other.

Some soils are young, others are middle-aged, others are mature, and still others are in a state of old age. Their ages depend primarily on the length of time they have remained in essentially the same place since they began to be formed, and on the nature of the climate. For example, soils of deserts and those on steep hillsides tend to remain young, their older portions being continuously lost in erosion by wind and water. The soils of recently-exposed islands that have been shoved up out of the sea are young. Those now being formed from recently erupted volcanic material will remain young for many years.

Soils reach maturity and old age quickly under conditions of relatively level topography, reasonably heavy rainfall, and moderately warm temperatures. The younger the soil the greater its similarity in chemical make-up to that of the original rock from which it was derived. Thus a young soil of limestone origin will contain considerably more lime than an older soil that was derived from the same kind of rock. The older the soil the greater its tendency to reflect the nature of the climate and the natural vegetation rather than that of the original rock from which it was formed.

Mature soils in high-rainfall regions consist mostly of that portion of the rocks' mineral matter which plants do not need and cannot use. They are made up largely of oxides of silicon, aluminum, and iron, as such, or in combination with each other in mineral forms known as silicates. The supplies of the plant-required mineral nutrients that remain in the soil are what were left over after the rains of the centuries had dissolved all they could of them and carried them out to sea.

Nevertheless, sufficient quantities of these mineral nutrients remain in the soil in available forms to meet the needs of plants growing under natural conditions. It is only after man has entered the picture and has grown, harvested, and sold crops, or the animal products produced by feeding them, that deficiencies of these mineral nutrients begin to develop.

It has been said that "soil is the one indestructible, immutable asset that the nation possesses, the one resource that cannot be used up." In a sense, this is true. Unfortunately, exposed soil is subject to being moved from place to place by wind and water. It may be carried far away from the place where it was formed only to be laid down on top of other better or poorer soil, as the case may be. Or it may be carried out and dumped into the ocean, where it is no longer available for use. And even if the soil remains in place its productivity will decline markedly with continued cropping or grazing. Thus, soil is indestructible only if it is tightly sewed to the earth by roots of plants and only if the losses of mineral nutrients from the sale of crops and livestock or their products are compensated for. This is where manure and composts and the lime and fertilizer industries enter the picture.

Under natural conditions the nutrient elements that still remain attached to the virtually insoluble yet very slowly dissolving soil continue to be made available for plant use. When such vegetation as weeds, grass, or trees is permitted to grow up and fall back onto the land, as happens in nature, the productivity of the underlying soil gradually increases. Each successive year's growth of such plants feeds on not only the mineral nutrients released by the rotting of previous plants but on any newly dissolved mineral nutrients that may have been released from the almost, but not entirely, insoluble mineral portion of the soil as well. The carbonic, nitric, and other acids resulting from microbial action on soil organic matter aid in the dissolving process.

Under agricultural conditions, with removal and sale of crops and livestock products from the farm, yields of unaided soil tend to fall off to ever lower levels. But the soil never becomes sterile. It will continue to support some type of vegetation under even the worst systems of management. If permitted to go back to nature, recovery of productivity may be fairly rapid. In the drier regions the natural vegetation will be mostly grass and weeds. In the more humid regions it will normally be trees.

The climate and its associated vegetation that acted on the original rocks to form soil, the nature of these rocks, and the length of time involved in the soil-forming processes have varied greatly from region to region. Such factors as glacial action, volcanic eruptions, wind erosion, and the deposition of river sediments on flooded lands may have been involved. Consequently, there are a considerable number of very different kinds of soil. These have been arranged for convenience into some three dozen Great Soil Groups. Of these one-half dozen can be used to advantage for illustrative purposes.

Russian scientists were responsible for the development of the first systematic scheme for grouping soils on the basis of climatic and vegetative factors. If one takes the train from Odessa to Moscow, whether by way of Kiev or Kharkov, he will travel over more than one thousand miles of flat to rolling plains that are covered with deep black soil, which the Russians named chernozem, meaning "black earth." This is the great wheat belt of the Ukraine. A peculiar fact about this deep black soil is the whitish layer of a limestonelike deposit that is found in the subsoil.

Chernozems were formed under conditions of a natural

grass cover. The explanation for the calcareous layer in the subsoil is found in the limited rainfall, which was sufficient to grow grass but not enough to permit very large amounts of the water to percolate through the subsoil and empty into the underground drainage channels. The most soluble substances in the soil, however, were carried away by the drainage waters. The lime, being much less soluble than some of the other soil constituents, was carried down only into the subsoil where it was redeposited, because much of the water that carried it down later moved back upward and was lost by evaporation from the surface of the soil or was transpired by plants.

The same kind of deep black soils are found in a number of other regions over the earth where climatic conditions are essentially the same as those in the Ukraine. In the United States they, and their close relatives, cover an extensive area from North Dakota southward to the Río Grande and eastward across Illinois and into Indiana. Other large areas of these black soils are found in southern Canada, northern Argentina, central Rumania, and South Africa.

North of the Ukraine in Russia is another large area of quite different soil. The temperatures of this area are lower, the rainfall is greater, and the rate of evaporation of water from the surface of the soil is less than in the Ukraine. As a result, not only have the readily soluble soil substances been carried away by the rainwater but the lime as well. The Russians named these soils podzols, meaning "ashes." The explanation for this name lies in a highly bleached grayish-white layer that is found just below the fertile layer of topsoil.

These gray to gray-brown soils were formed under conditions of a natural forest cover. They are dominant throughout central Europe. In North America they extend southward from eastern Canada to the cotton belt and from Minnesota eastward to Nova Scotia. Similar soils are found in the temperate zones of South America. Most of these soils are strongly acid naturally, or they soon become so after being farmed. They require liming for optimum yields of crops. Some of the finer clay particles of these soils have been carried down into the subsoils, sometimes to the extent of developing layers that are almost impermeable to water.

In the tropics, where rainfall is heavy and the natural cover is an almost impenetrable forest, one is impressed by the deep red color of the soil. This color has led to the soil's being named latosol, a word derived from the Latin *later*, meaning "brick." Over the centuries these soils have developed as a result of the drastic dissolving action of heavy rainfall under hot temperatures and the rapid rotting of soil organic matter. They have lost not only their readily soluble substances and their less soluble lime but a large part of their silicate silica as well.

Silica, the oxide of silicon, exists in soils in the form of virtually insoluble grains of quartz sand and in silicate minerals in which silica is joined to iron and aluminum oxides. Most soils contain 75 per cent or more silica in these two forms. But the silica of the silicates in latosols has been dissolved in large part and carried away by the drainage water. Latosols are essentially iron and aluminum oxides, with some free quartz.

In marked contrast to the tropical forests that cover the latosols, the gray-red desert soils may be almost completely bare of vegetation because of the limited rainfall in the regions where they exist. Strong winds and extreme variations in temperature have been primarily responsible for breaking the rocks to pieces to form these soils. Because of the low rainfall, the soluble substances, called salts, may never have been carried off by water. In that event, they may present a very troublesome problem when irrigation water is supplied.

The Great American desert, covering a large part of California, New Mexico, Idaho, and Utah and extending into the neighboring states, has an area of about 250,000 square miles, or over 150,000,000 acres. Similar large desert areas are found in Mexico and Chile. And much larger deserts are located in North Africa, central Asia, and the interior of Australia.

Along all the rivers of the earth, large and small alike, are soils that are made up of sediments that were carried downstream from higher levels in time of flood and spread out over the lowlands that the water overflowed. The farther downstream toward the river's mouth, the wider the area that was flooded and the deeper the river-borne deposits of sand, silt, and clay. These deposits, derived from a great variety of upstream soils, constitute what are known as alluvial soils. Such deposits are often fifty feet or more in depth. When drained, alluvial soils are usually highly productive, many successive layers of rich sediment often having been piled up on top of each other over long periods of time.

These alluvial soils underlie some of the most important food-producing areas of the earth. The valleys of the Tigris and Euphrates rivers in Iraq, the valley of the Ganges River in India, the Nile River Valley in Egypt, the valleys of the Amazon and La Plata rivers in South America, the Rhine River Valley in Holland and Germany, and the Mississippi River Valley provide some of the best examples of such soils.

The thirty or more other Great Soil Groups of the earth are made up of soils with properties between or beyond those of the five groups mentioned. One of these, the tundras, is of special interest because its subsoils remain frozen the year round. The topsoils may thaw out to sufficient depth each summer to permit the growth of grasses, mosses, lichens, and algae that form a mat over the surface. This makes the tundras highly useful for grazing purposes for livestock, notably for great herds of reindeer.

Tundras cover large areas in northern Alaska and Canada

and in northern Russia. Deep down they are rich in all mineral nutrients since, except by surface runoff, they have experienced little loss by way of drainage waters, the subsoils having been frozen for many centuries. It is possible that something could be done to increase their absorption of heat from the summer sun, and surface application of some black substance, such as powdered coal, has been suggested for this purpose.

One of the most troublesome problems in irrigated arid areas is that of the saline or salt-rich soils that tend to develop. The difficulty lies in the high concentrations of highly soluble salts of the type that have been dissolved by rainwater and carried out to sea in regions of heavy rainfall. When the salt content of these saline soils becomes excessive, plants will no longer grow on them. When water is applied to them, the salts tend to accumulate on the surface as the water evaporates.

Considerable effort has been and is being expended in preventing the accumulation of these salts to toxic concentrations. In addition to applying irrigation water in excess, use is sometimes made of massive moldboard plows that bury the accumulated salts below the level to which crop roots normally extend. Of these salts, sodium carbonate, of which washing soda is made, is the most troublesome, not only because of its high solubility in water but because of its strong alkalinity as well. Few plants will tolerate any considerable amount of this salt in the soil water.

The great glaciers, which once spread over a large part of northern North America, Europe, and Asia and the southernmost part of South America, played highly important parts in soil formation. The moving ice pulverized and mixed many different kinds of rock materials over which they moved. The soils derived from these glacial deposits are generally deep and relatively rich in the mineral elements required by plants They often contain abundant supplies of most of the additional mineral elements required by animals and man as well. Yet the warmer climate that has prevailed since the last invasion of the glaciers, some eleven thousand years ago, has so dominated the soil-forming process that the now prevailing soils belong to the Great Soil Groups associated with the present climate rather than with that of the more distant past.

During the glacial periods, which covered several hundred thousand years, strong winds carried large amounts of finely pulverized rock, now known as loess, off the exposed rock debris as the ice retreated, and deposited them over large areas of the earth's surface. A wide belt of such deposits extends from the Rocky Mountains eastward into Pennsylvania and as far south as the Mississippi Delta. Similar loess deposits are found over extensive areas in eastern Europe, in Siberia, and in South America. Some of these deposits were two hundred feet or more in thickness. Loess of nonglacial origin underlies the soils of much of China.

The soil formed from loess eventually took on the characteristics of the Great Soil Groups associated with the present climates of these regions. Knowledge that the loess was there before the present soils were developed has been obtained by studying the underlying deposits. When exposed, as along a railway right of way or a deep cut for a highway, loess often tends to maintain the side of the cut as it was made, vertical or otherwise. The silt particles of which loess is mostly made often fit together so tightly that they are not easily eroded out of position.

Large expanses of land are covered with volcanic ash in regions where eruptions have occurred at some time in the past. This ash consists of finely pulverized rock materials that were released into the surrounding atmosphere. It was often carried long distances in the direction of the prevailing winds and deposited as a coating over whatever was there before to form what has since become some of the most productive soil on earth. Such deposits are found on wide expanses of land in Java, Sumatra, and other islands on that part of the earth. They were also laid down over large areas in Australia and New Zealand. And they are found in localized areas in the United States, Central America, and other parts of the earth.

When the Gunung Kelut volcano in the eastern part of central Java erupted in 1919, an estimated 40 billion cubic meters of boulders, pumice, and ash were thrown into the air. The ash was widely distributed over long distances round about. This is only one of many such happenings. Ash of this type is weathered into soil in a relatively short period of time. Many of the soils derived from volcanic ash have not had time as yet to mature, being still in a very youthful and highly productive state.

Up to this point consideration has been given primarily to the effect of the climate and its related vegetation on the chemical properties of the soils that developed from the original rock cover. But these agents affected the size and arrangement of the soil particles, or the physical properties of soils, as well. The words "sand," "silt," and "clay" are used to indicate the sizes of soil particles. Agreements on the size limits of these particles have been reached by the International Society of Soil Science. The diameter limits of particles of coarse sand have been set between 2.0 and 0.2 mm. (one inch equals 25 mm.), those of fine sand between 0.2 and 0.02mm., those of silt between 0.02 0.002 mm., and those of clay less than 0.002 mm. These particles are not necessarily spheres, the diameters mentioned being those of their longest dimensions.

On a particle-size basis, soils are divided into classes in accordance with the size or sizes that are dominant. Thus, there are sand, silt, and clay soils, with all the possible gradations in between. Among these in-betweens are loams, sandy loams, silt loams, silty clay loams, and clay loams. A true loam is made up of about equal percentages of sand, silt, and clay. Relatively more sand is found in the sandy loams, but not necessarily a very large percentage more. And the same principle applies to the other loams.

Extensive areas of sandy soils are found on the coastal plains of the several continents, around the shores of lakes, or in areas where the soil was largely derived from the underlying sandstone. The whole of Florida lies on the coastal plains of the Atlantic Ocean and the Gulf of Mexico. The sandiness of these soils is due to the sorting-out process that occurred while the river waters that flowed out from the interior highlands were dropping their loads of sediment as they flowed into the sea. The seacoast was shoved out farther and farther into the sea as the larger sand particles separated out and dropped to the bottom when the velocity of the river waters was slowed down by the impact with the water in the sea.

The dunes around lakes are deposits of sand that have been moved by winds from the lake shore to build up surrounding higher land. The sandy soils that are found in the interiors of continents have been developed from sandstone as it weathered into the soil. This sandstone had been laid down long ago as sand along the shore of some ancient sea or lake and had been consolidated into rock by the pressure of materials deposited on top of it. Finally, it was pushed up out of the water by some tremendous subterranean force and, in time, it may have again been reduced to a sandy soil.

Large deposits of plant remains often accumulate in swamp areas to form peat. Such deposits are frequently built up to depths of fifty feet or more. The soils that form from these deposits, often known as mucks, consist mostly of organic matter, but they also contain varying amounts of mineral matter in the form of sand, silt, and clay. The properties of these peat soils differ greatly from those of the mineral soils. In some parts of the world peat is used extensively for fuel. Our present coal deposits were once deep deposits of peat, which were compressed into a compact state by heavy overburdens of rock-derived sediments that subsequently came to occupy positions on top of the peat deposits as they settled deeper into the sea.

When drained, peat soils have one important advantage over mineral soils: they are high in organic matter and its associated nitrogen, a very important air-derived plant nutrient. Over the centuries, this nitrogen had been captured from the gaseous supply in the air by electrical and microbial means, brought to the earth in combined form, used by plants, and stored in their tissues. And peat, like all other forms of plant refuse, constitutes a highly important source of food for the many millions of microbes that grow in it, once the excess water in which it was laid down has been drained off. Some of the more soluble mineral nutrients originally present in the peat-forming plant refuse have been carried away in the water overflow, this being particularly true of potassium, a highly important mineral nutrient for plants.

Soil is such an important natural resource that careful surveys have been and are being made to find out more about the kinds of soil in each nation, state, and county, and often on each farm and field. The starting point is usually a generalized survey that maps the land in large units, such as sand, silt, and clay soils, and valleys, prairies, plains, deserts, mountains, and swamps. The resulting maps may be made on the basis of one inch for every one hundred miles.

To meet more specific needs, soil maps of important agricultural areas may be made on the basis of one inch per mile. Such mapping is done not only in relation to the use to which the land is currently being put but to the potential agricultural uses to which it is best adapted. Such mapping includes consideration not only of the physical properties of the soils, but the lay of the land, its tendency to suffer from wind and water erosion, and its suitability for the growing of specific crops.

For still more detailed use by an individual farmer, land may be mapped on the basis of four or more inches to the mile. Such maps, in color, provide the needed information in such detail as to be highly useful to the man farming the land. These maps indicate the land that is so subject to erosion that it had best be kept in grass or trees. And they indicate the land that is best suited to particular crops, due consideration being given in each case to the measures that must be taken to prevent undue loss of soil by wind and water erosion.

Soil is a renewable natural resource, in contrast to coal, oil, gas, and ores, which are removed from their points of origin and never replaced. The same soil can be used and re-used year after year in perpetuity for the growing of crops, grasses, or trees, providing adequate measures are taken to keep it in place and to renew the supplies of mineral nutrients that are carried off the farm in harvested crops and in livestock or its products.

The Earth is round and like a ball,
Seems swinging in the air,
A sky extends around it all
And stars are shining there.

—PETER PARLEY

Chapter Two

THIS EARTH OF OURS

EARTH is a minute fragment of a universe that is believed to have come into existence as a result of a cataclysmic explosion of a single mass of highly concentrated matter some ten billion years ago. Out of this explosion evolved the galaxies, such as our Milky Way, that are made up of the many billions of stars that are known to exist in the heavens.

All of these stars, of which Sun is one, have been rushing farther and farther out into space at an extremely rapid rate ever since. But this rate is now believed to be slowing down. If so, eventually this expanding movement may come to a halt and its direction may then be reversed. In that event all the separate units of the universe might be pulled back together with a resulting new explosion that would repeat the sequence.

Where Earth had its origin and how it came to be have long been subjects of much speculation among mathematicians and astronomers, geologists and biologists, physicists and chemists, and philosophers and theologians. Some of the more modern concepts of highly capable scientists especially concerned with this subject appear sufficiently conclusive to make it possible to accept them as working hypotheses. But they still leave many points to be more fully explained.

Earth, located some 93 million miles out in space from Sun and revolving around it once every 365 days at a speed of about twenty-two miles a second, is believed to be an offshoot from Sun. It came into existence largely as a gaseous mass that began to solidify into its present form some four and one-half billion years ago. It is the third of a series of nine planetary satellites of Sun, of which Mercury and Venus are nearer to Sun, and Mars, Jupiter, Saturn, Uranus, Neptune, and Pluto are increasingly farther away from it. The distance from Sun to Pluto is estimated at 3,675 million miles.

Our solar system is not unique, and neither is Earth. Many millions of such systems are believed to exist in the universe. The number of stars, among the largest of which our sun is a mere midget, has been estimated at 10^{20}, which means 10 multiplied by itself 20 times. And of these millions of millions of millions of stars, some 10^{8} have been estimated to have planetary systems similar to the one of which Earth is a part. From this, one may speculate that there are millions of planets that are so located with reference to the stars round which they revolve as to have conditions that are favorable for life. The living forms on these Earthlike planets may be very different from those with which we are familiar. Conceivably, the highest forms of life on some of these plants may be superior to man.

The history of Earth is recorded in part in the rocks that are exposed to view and that have been reached by quarrying and boring. For convenience, this history is divided into five eras, of which the most recent, the Cenozoic era, covers the last 60 million years, since the folding that formed the Rocky Mountains. The next earlier Mesozoic era, extending back 130 million years farther, began with the folding that formed the Appalachian Mountains. Prior to that were the Paleozoic era of 360 million years following an extended period of widespread overflows of molten lava, the Proterozoic era of 900 million years after the Laurentian revolution, and the Archeozoic era that began in obscurity. These five eras total 2,000 million years, leaving 2,500 million more years to get us back to the beginning of time on Earth.

During the pre-Archeozoic era, Earth was a molten mass, the surface of which was cooling down to form a solid crust of rock. The moist vapor that originally surrounded Earth gradually condensed to form water. This existed mostly as such, but some of it joined to the minerals that formed as the molten rock cooled, and now exists in combined solid form. But the interior of Earth has remained hot down to the present time, the temperature of its central core being estimated to be at least 1,500°C.

The distance from the surface to the center of Earth is a little over 3,950 miles. The most dependable information about the interior of Earth has been obtained by studies of earthquake waves. When the rates of travel of these waves were measured at varying distances from their points of origin, they were found to increase to about eight miles a second at a depth of 1,800 miles, after which they slowed down to about five miles a second. From this it was deduced that Earth's core is made up of very different materials from that constituting the remainder of the globe. The average density of the rocks that make up the outside shell of Earth is about 2.7. That of Earth as a whole is

5.52. In other words, the weight of Earth is a little over five and one-half times that of an equal volume of water.

From this and other evidence the conclusion has been reached that Earth is enclosed within a shell about 750 miles thick. The outside of this shell consists of a relatively thin layer of soil, some rock debris, and a variety of solid rocks of the type with which we are familiar. The solid rock still lower down is probably a dark-colored igneous type, formed directly from molten matter and known as magma, of which little if any has ever been exposed to view. Within this outside shell is a second shell that is made up mostly of iron oxide and iron sulfide and that extends 1,050 miles farther inward toward the center of Earth. Inside this second shell is a core, with a radius of about 2,150 miles, that is believed to consist mostly of iron and nickel, similar in composition to most of the meteorites. The density of the iron oxide-sulfide inner shell is estimated at 5.6 and that of the inner iron-nickel core at 8.0. These three divisions of Earth's interior no doubt merge into each other rather than having distinct boundaries.

The temperature of Earth's central core is higher than that of the molten rock that is poured out of the craters of live volcanoes. Nevertheless, by reason of the mass of material that surrounds it, this core is essentially a solid. In this case again we are dealing only with a hypothesis, but one that is accepted as being a highly useful concept. The greatest depth to which Earth has been penetrated by drilling downward from the surface is about four miles, a superficial distance in comparison to the nearly one thousand times this that would be required to reach its center.

As Earth cooled down originally, its crust passed through a semisolid to a solid state, with great folds developing on its surface. Water collected in the valleys between these folds to form lakes and seas. Terrific tensions and pressures were built up within Earth's interior with the result that high mountain ranges, such as those of the Himalayas, the Alps, and the Rocky Mountains, were shoved up above the surrounding terrain.

Sudden underground slippages of great masses of rock frequently occurred. These opened up huge cracks, known as faults, which are horizontal displacements of soil and rock that can often be traced across the country for distances of one hundred miles or more. Proof of these and other great stresses, that developed within Earth's crust during the cooling process and subsequently, is found also in the transformation of limestone to marble, of shale to slate, and of bituminous coal to anthracite. Such metamorphoses could have taken place only under conditions of extremely high pressures and temperatures.

Undoubtedly, earthquakes were more frequent and catastrophic in the far distant past than they have been during historic time. But no person was there to see and record them. In the four thousand years of recorded history an estimated 13,000,000 people have been killed by earthquakes. During the earthquake that shattered the city of San Francisco in 1906 a great fault opened up that broke gas and water mains, resulting in terrifying fires that could not be brought under control and in much loss of life and property. In 1923 some 90,000 people lost their lives during an earthquake in Tokyo, Japan. An estimated 100,000 casualties resulted from an earthquake in northern Turkey in 1939.

Terrifying and highly destructive volcanic eruptions frequently follow earthquakes, the volcanoes belching forth great masses of molten rock, large volumes of flaming gases, and such vast quantities of ashes that often the sun is blotted out for many miles around. Some 2,500 volcanic eruptions have been recorded, of which over 2,000 have taken place in the Pacific Ocean region. More than 450 of these eruptions have occurred within historic times. The most famous volcanic eruption was that of Mount Vesuvius in A.D.79, which completely buried the cities of Pompeii and Herculaneum near Naples, Italy, killing thousands of people and destroying all the living things about the nearby countryside. In 1908 the city of Messina, Italy, was totally destroyed by such an eruption, some 85,000 people being killed. As recently as 1943 a mountain of molten rock and ashes was piled up to a height of two thousand feet within a few days in the center of what had been a prosperous farming community near Paricutin, Mexico. About 80 per cent of the known active volcanoes on Earth are of the submarine type, such as the one that shoved up a new island among the Azores in 1957. The Hawaiian Islands are of volcanic origin, having been built up at some points to a height of fourteen thousand feet above sea level from a starting base that was at least that far below it.

Associated with the high temperatures that result in the volcanic eruptions that continue to occur from time to time and from place to place are the large amounts of steam and boiling water that come to the surface in many parts of Earth. Old Faithful Geyser in Yellowstone National Park, which erupts quite regularly about once an hour the year round and has been doing so for many years, is a good example. At Hot Springs, Arkansas, forty-seven such hot-water springs, with reputed curative values, attract many thousands of visitors every year. The most extensive and long-continued hot springs known are located in New Zealand and in Iceland, where they are of great importance because of their heat value during the cold and extended winter periods.

Earthquakes are often closely followed by what have long been termed tidal waves that have been known to travel across the ocean at speeds up to 450 miles an hour with disastrous effects when they reach a shore. This term is a misnomer in that these waves have no connection with tides. A better word, coined by the Japanese, who have had a great deal of experience with them, is tsunami. Japan has been hit by more than a dozen tsunamis within the last half-dozen years, eight of them highly destructive. One of these, on June 15, 1960, is estimated to have destroyed ten thousand homes and to have killed 27,000 people. In 1883 a tsunami, originating as a result of an eruption of Mount Krakatoa in the South Pacific, had a height of well over one hundred feet as it rolled in on the adjacent islands of Sumatra and Java, drowning many thousands of people. This wave was recorded on tidal gauges as far away as the English Channel.

Earthquakes, volcanoes, and tsunamis have had far-reaching effects on the topography of the land and on the floor of the sea. But they have not had as much effect on the whole as the continuously operating cold, heat, wind, and rain. These forces break the surface rocks down into smaller and smaller pieces and have marked dissolving and transporting effects. Some idea of the rate of movement of rock and soil debris by the water that falls as rain is provided by the estimated two million tons of sediment that is being carried down to the mouth of the Mississippi River and dumped into the Gulf of Mexico every year. Thus the mountains and hills tend to be worn away and the ocean floor to be built up with the material that is carried off them. The Appalachian Mountains, which came into existence as a result of a strong upward thrust from deep beneath the surface of Earth some 200 million years ago, are believed originally to have rivaled the European Alps in height.

Most of what is now dry land was once located beneath the sea. Consequently, most of the soil cover, which is relatively thin, is underlain by sedimentary rocks, the type that has been formed from the cementing together of the land-derived rock debris after it had been laid down on the ocean floor. In some regions, however, great volumes of lava have been poured out over the surface of the land since it emerged from the sea. A large part of Arizona and New Mexico, for example, is overlain by such lava beds and by the associated volcanic ash. Here and there huge extrusions of molten rock from lower depths have been shoved up almost to the surface to form what are known as batholiths. One such mass of rock underlies an area of sixteen thousand square miles in Idaho.

Sometime within the many millions of years during which the original igneous rocks were being distintegrated by the forces of nature and the sedimentary rocks were being formed on the ocean floor, the first simple forms of life came into being, probably in the ooze along the ocean shore and probably at more than one location. This has been the subject of a great deal of speculation, and some highly interesting hypotheses have been developed. An international symposium on the origin of life was held in Moscow in 1957. Most of those present apparently believed that the starting points for life were the simpler amino acids—the substances that, when joined together, form proteins, which are key compounds in living things. These amino acids are believed to have been formed as a result of lightning discharges that joined the constituents of the atmosphere. The first evidence of life is found in the sedimentary rocks of the latter part of the Archeozoic era, some 1,500 million years ago. It was essential that conditions become favorable for life before it could develop. And when such conditions came to be, life developed as a natural consequence. Possibly life is still originating in these same primitive forms.

The first forms of life were certainly single-celled microscopic organisms. But more complex forms of life gradually evolved. By the time the Proterozoic era had arrived the simpler forms of algae, worms and crustaceans, and the forerunners of the fishes had appeared, as evidenced by the fossil forms that are found embedded in the sedimentary rocks of that era. During the latter part of that era, some 600 million years ago, the whole of what is now the United States of America was submerged in the sea, and extensive deposits of limestone were being laid down on its surface.

During the Paleozoic era that followed, many kinds of fishes, the giant ferns, and the antecedents of the great reptiles evolved. During the Carboniferous period of that era, something over 200 million years ago, the larger part of the eastern third of the United States lay beneath a shallow inland lake. Vast swamps covered most of the region where Ohio, Pennsylvania and the Virginias are now located. Great quantities of lush vegetation grew up, died, and fell back into the swamps to form deep beds of peat. Subsequently, these peat beds were completely submerged and covered deeply with deposits of sediment that later were consolidated into rock. The tremendous pressures of these overlying rock deposits on the peat transformed it into bituminous coal.

By the time of the arrival of the Mesozoic era the huge dinosaurs, crocodiles, and tortoises had evolved. About the middle of this era, some 125 million years ago, the various types of giant reptilelike birds came into being. Bones of many of these long-extinct animals are found from time to time in excavating the various sedimentary rock formations of that era, and many of these bones have been assembled in skeletal form in natural history museums.

The dinosaur and other giant forms of animal life went out of existence sometime during the latter part of the Mesozoic era. The tendency toward gigantism during the early part of that era and the disappearance of these enormous animals before the end of the era remain to be explained. One suggested answer to their disappearance is that the predatory types of smaller mammals that evolved to take the place of these giant forms destroyed the latter's eggs and young. In other words, the dinosaurs were either too sluggish to protect their eggs and young or else they had little or no parental interest in them.

Insects, which had appeared in primitive form as far back as the Carboniferous period of the Paleozoic era, possibly 225 million years ago, developed in great variety and numbers during the latter part of the Mesozoic era. The first snakes also evolved then, as evidenced by fossil forms in the sedimentary rocks of that period. Flowering plants, trees, and grasses were well developed by the end of that era.

The Cenozoic era, the one in which we live, saw the development of the first primitive forms of apes, elephants, deer and horses into their present forms. Flowering plants dominated the vegetation. During the last million years of this era, in what is known as the Pleistocene period, great masses of ice that were many feet in thickness pushed southward from the Arctic regions. These deep ice sheets, or glaciers, covered the whole of Canada and extended as far south as the Ohio River. And sometime during that period the forerunner of man appeared.

Six successive invasions of the glaciers are recorded in the rock refuse that was left behind when the glaciers retreated after each advance. The ice finally withdrew into the Arctic regions, beginning about eleven thousand years ago. Similar records of glacial invasions are found in northern Europe and over the southern tip of South America. Variations in temperature were the immediate causes of the advances and retreats of these glaciers. When the next invasion will occur, if ever, remains to be determined. But the evidence suggests that the climate of North America and of northern Europe may become much warmer than it is now before it becomes much colder.

It is now necessary to return to the task of defining somewhat more exactly the conditions that existed on Earth during its earlier history in relation to those that now prevail. Two highly important variables must be considered. These are the changes in climate that have occurred over the billions of years of Earth's existence and the changes in elevation of the various parts of Earth's crust.

During the Carboniferous period of the Paleozoic era the most important coal deposits of Earth were being laid down. During that period the climate of the regions where this was being done, including the east central portion of the United States, must have been similar to that of the present humid semitropical regions. During the Pleistocene period of the Cenozoic era, beginning about 150 million years later, glaciers were advancing into and retreating from these same regions.

Throughout the later eras of Earth's history, after the solid crust had formed and the water had settled into the vast depressions to become the seas that surround the land, the elevations of the present land areas alternated between those far above the level of the sea and those far beneath its surface.

When the land was above sea level it was being subjected to the action of wind and water, aided by the abrasive action of sand and ice. The rock was expanding and contracting with alternate heat and cold, resulting in its breaking to pieces. And the water that ran off the land, acting on the underlying rock and soil in association with the carbonic acid contained in it, was dissolving substances and carrying them out to sea. The simpler forms of plant life that came into existence excreted carbonic acid that etched the surfaces of the rocks on which they grew. The roots of the larger plants shoved their way down into the cracks of underlying rocks to expand them further. And when the plants died and dropped back to Earth the soil microbes that abounded fed on their remains, releasing stronger acids, such as nitric and sulphuric, with still greater solvent effects on rock and soil. Thus the land was leveled downward and the ocean floor was built up from the debris, including great accumulations of some of the salts that had been dissolved out of soil and rock.

Among the rock-derived salts in the sea were great quantities of calcium and magnesium carbonates that eventually settled out from the water and fell to the bottom where they were gradually solidified into limestone rock. Additional quantities of these carbonates were used in shell formation, such as are found in coral reefs. And when these vast deposits of limestone were subsequently shoved up out of the sea they formed a highly important underpinning for the soil that was formed out of the top layers and left behind as a deposit on the surface of the still unaffected limestone rock beneath.

The land itself and the floor of the surrounding sea were being raised and lowered over great distances as a result of catastrophic happenings inside Earth over very long periods of time. Consequently, the deepness of the sea and the distance from the shore of any given spot varied greatly from time to time. Near the shore, sand deposits were being laid down, and these were ultimately consolidated to form sandstone. Farther out from the shore, clays were being deposited, and these ultimately became shale. And still farther out, the salts of which limestone was made were being deposited on the bottom of the sea. Since the depths of the sea were quite variable over long periods, sandstone may have been formed at a given location at one period, shale at another, and limestone at yet another.

Once these deposits were laid down on the ocean floor, consolidated into rock, and then elevated above the level of the sea by some titanic subterranean force to become dry land, they were available for viewing when exposed, as on the sides of a canyon or of a cut along a railroad right of way, or in a quarry. And when they are examined in such locations, successive layers, or strata, of limestone, sandstone, and shale are found on top of each other, these strata varying between a few inches and many feet in thickness.

Beneath the relatively thin layer of soil that now covers the larger part of Earth's surface are the various kinds of rock from which soils were formed. For the most part these underlying rocks are the sedimentary types, but here and there they are the igneous types. During the Ice Age, rock debris of both the sedimentary and igneous types were intermingled as the tops of hills were torn away and the valleys were filled in. Large quantities of this mixed rock debris were left behind in what are known as terminal moraines. These are long deep ridges of large rocks, stones, gravel, sand, and rock flour extending east and west across the north central part of the United States. They mark the line where the ice was being melted as fast as it advanced southward, its rock burden being piled up continuously as the melting took place.

Over all these millions of years soluble salts were being dissolved out of the rocks and soil and these were accumulating in the surrounding seas. Some of these salts separated out and fell to the ocean floor. Others of these salts remained dissolved in the ocean water. From place to place arms of the ocean were cut off from the main body of water, the water evaporated, and the salts were left behind as white deposits. Later many of these deposits were covered over with rock and soil, often to a depth of several thousand feet. Most of the common salt that is used for seasoning food and the potash salts that are used for fertilizing purposes come from such underground deposits. The present ocean water contains about 3.5 per cent by weight of salts, of which common salt constitutes about 75 per cent.

Although the atmospheric elements tend to level the mountains and fill up the seas, much of land still stands high above the level of the ocean. The highest land elevation in the United

States, the top of Mount Whitney, is 14,495 feet above sea level and the highest in the world, the top of Mount Everest is 29,000 feet above it. Similarly there are great depths to the sea in some locations, the deepest spot, about 35,000 feet, being found just off the island of Mindanao, one of the Philippines. Some of the land in the interiors of the continents is lower than the surface of the sea. Thus Death Valley in California is 280 feet below sea level and the shore of the Dead Sea, between Jordan and Israel, is 1,290 feet below it.

And God said: Let the waters under the heavens be gathered together in one place and let the dry land appear. And it was so.

—GENESIS

Chapter Three
THE LAND ON WHICH WE LIVE

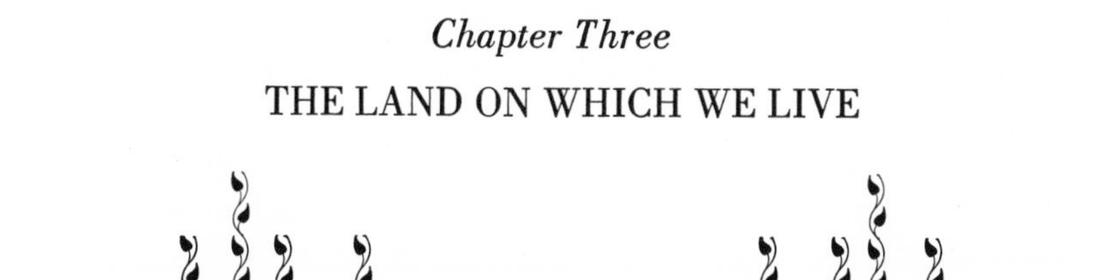

LEGEND has it that Atlantis, an island that was larger than Asia Minor and Libya with an archipelago of many lesser islands existed some twelve thousand years ago in the Atlantic Ocean just beyond the Pillars of Hercules at the Strait of Gibraltar. The armies of this once great nation were said to have overrun the region around the Mediterranean Sea for a long period. Plato wrote a history of Atlantis, recording that it had been engulfed by the sea following a terrific earthquake. Montaigne believed this and so did Voltaire.

Whether Atlantis ever existed and whether it disappeared beneath the sea or not—and the evidence indicates that it did not—other lesser areas of land are known to have suddenly disappeared from above the surface of the sea. The northern part of the island of Krakatoa in the East Indies, including its highest peak, was blown into the sea during a terrific explosion in 1883. Some of the islands of the ocean are merely the tops of mountains that once stood high above the water surrounded by considerable areas of lower-lying land. At one time a strip of land extended across what is now the Bering Strait from Alaska to Siberia, across which men and animals could pass at will. Out in the Atlantic Ocean what is known as the Atlantic Ridge extends from Iceland southward to the Equator and beyond for a total distance of some ten thousand miles. It rises from five to ten thousand feet above the ocean floor, but the top of the ridge is still a mile below sea level. There is good reason to believe that this may once have been dry land.

In certain parts of Earth the edges of the mainland are being slowly engulfed by the seas along the shores. Long Island, New York, for example, is known to be sinking at a rate of about two feet a century. The level of the land in Florida has been lowered at a rate of about three and one-half inches a year during the last fifteen hundred years. Most of continental United States, except for the part that is located north of a line drawn from Boston to Chicago and westward, is slowly sinking with reference to the level of the sea. Part of the explanation for this, however, may be found in rising sea levels.

If the glaciers of the Arctic regions, which now are virtually dormant, should grow and expand as far south as they did during the Ice Age, with a wall of ice that rose at some points to a height of two miles or more, the level of the water in the ocean might well be lowered three to four hundred feet, as more of the water that evaporated from the sea and fell on the land as rain was transformed into ice and added to that already there. This would result in exposing large areas of new land along the present ocean shore. Even as matters now stand, the level of the water in the ocean is measurably lower in the spring than in the fall.

Land as we now know it is that part of Earth's surface that is exposed above the level of the sea. Vast areas of it are relatively level plateaus, plains, and prairies. Other great areas are rolling to hilly. And much of the land is covered with high mountains. Then there are many low-lying swampy areas in which any rain that falls locally or on surrounding higher lands tends to accumulate. Some of the dry land lies below sea level, hemmed in by higher land between it and the ocean. Part of the Imperial Valley of California, for example, is more than two hundred feet below the level of the Pacific Ocean, which is less than two hundred miles away to the west.

Land has no fixed boundaries. Tides come and go. Waves are constantly battering the coasts. The great continental expanses of land are being continuously worn down by wind and water. The United States of America, for example, is being denuded at an estimated rate of one inch every 760 years. The rock and soil that are thus being carried downhill from higher to lower levels are being deposited in part on top of other low-lying rock and soil. But much of this material is being carried completely off the land by way of the rivers and piled up at their mouths to form wide expanses of new land that eventually can be put to use. Very large areas of such sediment-built delta lands are found at the mouths of the Mississippi, the Amazon, and the Rhine Rivers, to mention only a few.

New land is continuously being formed along the ocean shores by coral, in association with other marine forms of life. These coral reefs and atolls serve as collecting points for rock and soil sediments, often growing into considerable areas of land on which the large plants of the nearby body of drier land finally become established. The coral-formed Great Barrier Reef along the northeastern coast of Australia is about one thousand miles long and has a width varying between ten and twenty miles.

Large areas of land have been reclaimed from the sea by man in a number of countries. The best examples of this are found in the Netherlands, where such land-reclaiming operations have been under way since the sixteenth century. Over 500,000 acres have been added to the agricultural land of that country by such procedures. The land was diked off from the sea, and pumps were employed to remove the sea water and any excess water that fell as rain. Soluble salts left behind in the soil from sea water were carried off with the water during these pumping operations. After four or five years of these and other procedures, what was once sea bottom sediment became sufficiently free of sea salts to permit its being put to intensive agricultural use.

The land area of Earth is estimated at around 56 million square miles, or nearly 36 billion acres. This total area of land is only 28 per cent of the total surface area of Earth, the other 72 per cent being covered by sea water. And even within any given national or continental unit of land, a considerable portion is covered with water. Thus the total area within the mainland forty-eight states of the United States of America is 1,934 million acres, but 1.5 per cent of this, or 29 million acres, is fresh-water surface.

Asia constitutes about 30 per cent of the total land area of Earth; Africa, 21 per cent; North and Central America, 16 per cent; and South America, 12 per cent. Of the remainder, about 8 per cent is in Antarctica, 7 per cent in Europe, and 6 per cent in the islands of the oceans.

The larger part of this vast area of land is essentially useless in terms of agriculture. Much of it is overlain with sand, gravel, or solid rock. A great deal of it is so mountainous as to be virtually inaccessible to man. Large portions are swamp that is covered with almost impenetrable vegetation, as in the Amazon River Valley. Still larger portions in the polar regions are buried in snow and ice the year round. The subsoil of other large areas is permanently frozen, only the surface soil being thawed out sufficiently during the short summer seasons to permit the growth of vegetation, and this in only relatively limited quantities. And about 35 per cent of the land area of Earth is semiarid, arid, or desert.

Of the 33,000 million acres of actual land accounted for by the World Food and Agricultural Organization, about 3,000 million acres is being used for the production of food and fiber crops. This cropped land is the part that is most favorably located with respect to climate and topography and to convenience of access. Of the remaining 30,000 million acres, 5,300 million is in meadow and pasture, 8,700 million in forest and woodland, 1,000 million is unused but potentially productive, and 15,000 million acres is waste or built-over land.

Some 7,000 million acres could be put under cultivation. But to fit the extra 4,000 million acres for use in growing food and fiber crops would require large expenditures. The land would have to be cleared of brush, shrubs, and trees, drained or irrigated, or otherwise developed for farming by contouring or terracing, depending on the conditions that now prevail. These are often very expensive operations. Nevertheless, given time, the advantage of power machinery, and the will of the people to do the work, all of these improvements could be effected.

Some of this newly developed land would be as productive for grains and fibers, fruit and vegetables, sugar and alkaloid plants as that now being devoted to the production of these crops. But much of it would be far less productive. The cost per acre of operating large areas of this land would be relatively high. But if all of it were developed to a reasonably high state of production, it could be made to support a population several times that now inhabiting Earth.

In increasing agricultural production there is usually a choice between expanding the acreage that is being farmed and raising acre yields on that already in crops. The former is classed as horizontal expansion and the latter as vertical expansion. Taking both possibilities into consideration, the opportunities for increasing food and fiber production are very great indeed.

In addition to the 7,000 million acres of land that are now being plowed or that could be put to the plow, there is another 10,000 million acres or more that are being or could be used for grazing and forestry. Included among the grazing lands are the hilly to mountainous areas that have sufficient rainfall to support a good grass cover and that are accessible for such use. And there are large expanses of semiarid land that receive enough rainfall to support a sparse growth of grass and edible shrubs. Much of this land is now being overgrazed, notably in areas where sheep and goats predominate. This applies particularly to the Mediterranean countries and to the Near East. By controlled grazing and better systems of pasture management, the productive capacity of much of this grazing land could probably be doubled.

Much of the 8,700 million acres of land now in forest and woodland has no management whatever applied to it, except that of nature herself. By constructive intervention on the part of man, such as has long been practiced by the more progressive nations of Western Europe and is being put into operation on an ever larger scale in North America and in other parts of the world, the yields of these forests could be greatly increased.

Grasslands and forests have value not only for the grazing and wood they produce but in preventing loss of soil in the runoff, protecting the land against the erosive action of wind, and adding to the aesthetic enjoyment of the people who pass alongside or walk through them. Much of the land that is being grazed or is growing trees serves as a reserve that can be put to the plow in case of need. And, in case of emergency, wood can be processed into quite satisfactory feed for livestock and even into food for man.

About 40 per cent of Earth's total land area, or some 13,000 million acres, has little or no vegetative cover. This is largely because the climate under which this land is located is either too dry or too cold to permit any very great amount of plant growth. In some cases, however, it is because the land is too wet or the climate too hot. Included in this nonproductive land are the many acres that are being used for industrial, city, highway, and similar purposes.

Irrespective of its character or the nature of its environment, land provides a stable location on which man can live and from which he can operate in developing a satisfactory means of livelihood for himself and family. Having established himself on the land, the coal, oil, gas, and mineral wealth that lies hidden beneath the surface is his to search for and, having found, to make use of as he sees fit. The water that surrounds the land, the air and space above it, the sunshine and rain that fall on it, and any produce that grows from it are at his disposal.

Virtually all land has possibilities for development in one way or another. Deserts can be irrigated, and the quantity of water currently at man's disposal for this purpose will be materially increased in due time. Eroded lands can be brought back into use. Irregularly surfaced lands can be leveled. Hillsides can be farmed on the contour and terraced. Swamps can be drained. Jungles can be cleared. And crops can be developed by breeding and selection to withstand much greater extremes of drouth, wetness, heat, or cold.

Some of the deserts are underlain with mineral wealth. The flat gray-brown desert region extending north and south for some 450 miles in the northern part of Chile has long been worked for nitrate for fertilizer purposes. The width of this nitrate deposit area, known as the "Pampa," varies between ten and fifty miles. Shipments of nitrate from this area have totaled over 130 million tons and the present rate of production of around two million tons a year can be maintained for another century or more. Much of the petroleum of the world comes from desert regions such as those of Iran and Saudi Arabia. Increasing quantities of petroleum are now coming into the world market from beneath the Sahara Desert in Algeria.

The final factor that determines how far man can go in developing the land resources of Earth is the quantity of the various types of energy at his disposal. The desert has its own source of energy in the bright sun that shines on it the year round. This sunshine has much greater possibilities for use than are now being realized. Flowing water, wherever it may be, can be put to use for power purposes. The world's coal, petroleum, and oil-shale resources are very large indeed, and more remains to be discovered. And the potentialities for the use of nuclear energy are much greater than all the rest combined. Assuming the development of all these energy resources to the extent now thought possible, a great many more things can eventually be done to bring what is now essentially waste land into some type of useful production.

Waste land may have great value separate and apart from the growing of food and fiber crops or the development of underground mineral, coal, gas, and petroleum resources. The mountains, the swamps, the frozen lands, and the deserts, like the sea, have great value in terms of open space, where man is free to roam at will. They provide vast reaches of territory to be explored, even if only for the sake of satisfying some inner urge of man. And they offer great relief from the cares of everyday life. Many people are greatly oppressed by the crowds on city streets, the ever tightening space in the suburbs, and the ever-more-hurried traffic on the highways.

The untamed lands of Earth are a paradise for the traveler, the hunter, the fisherman, and the lover of wildlife, whether plant or animal. A mountain is a delight to the man who wants to climb it, whether merely for the sake of proving that he can do it or for the purpose of satisfying his curiosity about what is on the other side. The jungle and the desert have great appeal to those who enjoy the harsh struggle for survival that ensues when man pits his energies against the wild. And many explorers have suffered great hardships just to get a glimpse of the Arctic and Antarctic regions. The pioneers who took the Americas away from the Indians were that kind of people. No doubt the great urge of man to explore outer space finds its inception in an unborn but possibly unrecognized desire to escape from the ever growing pressures of our modern civilization.

Until quite recently, the pressures of growing populations were overcome by war, famine, and pestilence. Now that such catastrophes are, in ever larger degree, being brought under control, other means of release from these pressures are being sought. As a result the imagination of man has tended to expand farther and farther out into the unexplored land regions of Earth, the great expanses and depths of the sea, and the vast reaches of space. He feels entitled to the hope that he may be able to explore not only what lies beyond the horizon but what exists throughout the solar system and possibly far beyond it.

Returning to Earth, its land area as a whole would appear to be sufficient to provide living space in abundance for all the people now at hand and for many billions more. On the average, every person on Earth now has over ten acres of land at his disposal. Yet averages are highly misleading. In Japan the land area per person is only a little over one acre. In the Netherlands it is only four-fifths of an acre. And in the great cities of Earth, the area per person is measured in square feet.

The land resources of Earth are now quite well mapped, although many regions have never been fully explored. One reason for this was the discovery of the Americas by Columbus in 1492, which opened up a whole new hemisphere for exploration and development and attracted the attention of people from all over the world. For a time explorers were held back by the Indians, but pioneer pressures were so great that the Indians eventually had to yield. In spite of many disastrous happenings in connection with the exploitation of North, Central, and South America, the people of Europe quickly overran the entire hemisphere. The populations that were soon built up in the New World were not at any great expense to those of the Old World. The conditions for human reproduction were so favorable that rapid increase in numbers took place.

The United States of America provides an interesting example of the rate at which the land area per person decreases in a new world under conditions of a free society. Each of 800,000 Indians who inhabited what is now the mainland of this country when the first white man arrived on the scene had some 2,400 acres of land at his disposal. He and his fellows were free to roam at will over large areas of plain, prairie, plateau, mountain, desert, and valley, subject only to such limitations as were imposed by neighboring tribes. That was the situation when the first permanent English settlement was established at Jamestown, Virginia in 1607.

By 1706, the year Benjamin Franklin was born in Boston, the white population of this country had grown to an estimated 1,000,000, and the land area per person was about nineteen hundred acres. When Thomas A. Malthus' famous "Essay on the Principle of Population," which dealt with war, famine, and pestilence as the only dependable controls for population, was published in 1798, there were 5,000,000 white people in this country and the land area per person had been reduced to about four hundred acres. When, one hundred years later, Sir William Crookes addressed the British Association for the Advancement of Science on "Wheat," dealing with the problem of providing larger quantities of nitrogen fertilizers so that more wheat could be produced for the benefit of the wheat-eating peoples who then dominated the world, the population had grown to 75,000,000 and the land area per person had dropped to twenty-five acres. By 1960 the population had grown to over 180,000,000 and the area per person had been reduced to less than eleven acres. By the year 2000 the population of the United States is expected to be over 300,000,000 and the land area per person will be reduced to a little over six acres, including each person's share of mountain, swamp, and desert.

The mainland of the United States has a land area of 1,905 million acres. Of this about 150 million acres is desert, with an average annual rainfall of less than ten inches. Much of this desert is essentially devoid of vegetation. The remainder is covered with cactus and a variety of other virtually useless types of vegetation. Lying east of this desert, an area thirty times that of the state of New Jersey, is 600 million acres of land under a semiarid climate with an average annual rainfall of ten to twenty inches. Still farther east is an additional 300 million acres of land under semihumid conditions of twenty to twenty-five inches of rain per year. Here grain is being grown, with high acre yields in years of average rainfall or above and virtually no yield in years of drouth.

Some 27 million acres of these desert, arid, and semihumid lands is under irrigation. Enough more water is in sight for two-thirds that many million acres more. But over half the land area of the United States is still too dry for dependable production of harvested crops. The larger part of this is being used for grazing, an average of about seventy-five acres being required to support each steer or its equivalent weight of other forms of livestock. As matters now stand, the primary burden in feeding the people of the United States mainland rests on the more level portions of some 900 million acres of land, including about 850 million acres in the more humid regions and 45 million acres that is being or can be irrigated.

The one hundredth meridian is essentially the dividing line between the more favorable crop-growing region of eastern United States and the drier region to the west. This line extends southward across the central part of the Dakotas and Nebraska and somewhat west of central Kansas, Oklahoma, and Texas. Another smaller but highly important crop-producing area of adequate rainfall is found along the Pacific Coast, between the Cascade Range of mountains and the ocean.

Some 350 million acres of land in the United States is now being devoted to the production of harvested crops. Additional large acreages of cropland are temporarily in fallow, cover crops, or pasture, or they are lying idle. The total available cropland in 1960 was estimated at about 465 million acres. When the need arises, some 65 million acres of plowable pastureland, 18 million acres of irrigable arid land, 40 million acres of drainable wet land, and 100 million acres of woodland and forest land can also be put to the plow. Looking farther ahead, large acreages of salty marshland along our coasts could probably be put to agricultural use by diking, pumping, and otherwise preparing it for use. Additional land may someday be reclaimed from the sea along our shores, as the Dutch have done. Taking all these possibilities into consideration, it seems reasonable to believe that some 700 million acres of potentially well-watered land on the mainland could ultimately be brought into the production of harvested crops.

The land resources of Alaska, the forty-ninth state, constitute an additional 365 million acres. With a present population of 200,000, the land area per person is almost identical to that the Indians originally enjoyed on the mainland. But the evidence indicates that Alaska has much greater value for strategic military purposes, for its timber, oil, and mineral resources, and for recreational uses than it has for agriculture. With further industrial exploitation, Alaska is likely, on balance, to become a food-importing state. Hawaii, the fiftieth state, has a land area of only four million acres. With a population already exceeding one-half million, its net agricultural contribution to the other peoples of the United States will be relatively small in comparision to that of the mainland.

On the mainland good agricultural land is being lost to factories, cities, suburban developments, highways, and recreational areas at a rate of over one million acres a year. And the wind and water that are permitted to erode large areas of presently and potentially useful cropland are causing great damage, often beyond the point of repair. These losses of agricultural land are receiving the attention of conservation agencies, the largest being the federal Soil Conservation Service, which is closely allied to the Soil Conservation Districts. In an increasing number of localities, zoning commissions and similar agencies are now actively engaged in trying to prevent the use of good agricultural land for nonagricultural purposes.

On the other hand, industrial development has also been responsible for the restoration of large acreages of first-class farming land to food production. When tractors and automobiles replaced some twenty million horses and mules, it was no longer necessary to devote large acreages to growing the grain and hay that were needed to feed these work animals. And when the cotton used in the manufacture of clothing and for many other purposes was extensively replaced by synthetic fibers, still more land became available for food production. Large-scale synthesis of air-nitrogen fertilizers also released land on which food could be grown, it being no longer necessary to grow such extensive acreages of clover and other legumes to collect nitrogen from the air. Other technological advances will undoubtedly be instrumental in making still more land available for food production.

Ways and means designed specifically to transform nonagricultural land into agricultural land are being developed. Soil-moving equipment is being used on an ever larger scale to level land, fill in gullies, and improve land contour. Mesquite and other shrubs and browse are being uprooted from the soil by huge crawler type tractors with heavy blades that, in one operation, open up the land to a depth of a foot or more and drop seed of improved grasses over the upturned soil. A great deal of attention is being given to the possibilities of making it rain where more rain is needed and to reclaiming water from the sea for irrigating more arid land.

The land areas of Earth constitute a highly important natural resource. If adequately cared for, they can be made to produce food and fiber in abundance in perpetuity. Primitive man gave little thought to the land. Nature provided virtually everything he needed in abundant supply. And this was without effort on his part, save the plucking of the fruit from the shrubs, vines, and trees and the gathering of the grain that grew without his help. He could make use of natural caves and the boughs of trees in providing shelter from the elements. He could wander from place to place according to his desires. His primary problem was that of protecting himself and family from other wild men and from the wild beasts that abounded.

Man had the advantage of a brain that could be and was developed to make him the dominant form of life. In due time he and his neighbors gathered together with groups for self-protection. Eventually, these groups grew into communities, states, and nations, with boundaries that were defended. From then on, subsistence came mostly from within these boundaries.

As the population grew within any such land unit and there was less freedom of movement, a point was finally reached at which more food had to be provided than the land could produce in its natural state. So, some nine thousand years ago, domestication of wild plants and animals was begun. Land was cleared, worked with a forked stick, and planted to grain. Then it became necessary to care for this land to the end that it could be used year after year for crop production.

The recorded history of cropped land began with two great civilizations that developed, first in the valleys of the Tigris and Euphrates rivers of Iraq and later in the valley of the Nile River in Egypt. These civilizations were founded in arid regions, except for the valleys through which the rivers flowed and over which they poured their life-giving waters in time of flood. The water in these rivers originated far upstream in mountainous regions of high rainfall and heavy forests. The floods were gradually brought under control by the development of extensive systems of dams and irrigation canals.

Today, neither of these nations enjoys the prominence it once did. A great variety of explanations have been offered for this slow progress. First, it was known that the great prosperity of these early peoples aroused the acquisitive instincts of surrounding warring tribes. Both nations were repeatedly overrun by marauding armies during the course of their histories. The land was laid bare and the cities were destroyed. But the people recovered. Irrigation systems were repaired. Crops were again planted. Cities were rebuilt on top of the remains of the old ones. And these nations went ahead with renewed energy after each catastrophe. Yet a point was finally reached at which full recovery and quickly renewed advance after an armed invasion failed to take place. Today these once great nations are of more interest because of the immensity and high quality of the ruins of the civilizations that once were theirs than because of the agricultural and industrial prowess they now possess.

He who with pocket hammer smites the edge
Of luckless rock or prominent stone, disguised
In weather stains or crusted o'er by Nature
With her first growth, detaching by the stroke
A chip or splinter, to resolve his doubts;
And, with that ready answer satisfied
The substance classes by some barbarous name,
And hurries on; or from the fragments picks
His specimen, if not haply interveined
With sparkling mineral, or should crystal cube
Lurk in its cells, and thinks himself enriched,
Wealthier, and doubtless wiser, than before.

—WORDSWORTH

Chapter Four
OUR GRANITE BASE

VULCAN, the Roman god of fire in its most sinister aspect of devouring flames, and Pluto, the Greek god of the infernal regions to which the damned were doomed, are identified in the names of the igneous rocks that were formed when Earth solidified from its original completely molten state, the words volcanic and plutonic being used to designate the two great groups into which they are divided. The temperatures of the molten masses from which these rocks were formed must have been at least 1,250°C., or nearly 2,300°F.

Most of the rock that one sees about him is far removed in character and appearance from that of the original volcanic and plutonic types. About three-fourths of the land surface of

Earth is overlain by sedimentary rocks, beneath the covering layer of soil. These sedimentary rocks were formed out of materials that were derived from the original igneous rocks but that had undergone great changes in the weathering process.

The volcanic rocks now found exposed from place to place over the surface of Earth were formed from molten matter that was forced upward from depths of two to twenty miles below the surface and that was spread out over the surface, covering whatever was there before. These volcanic masses cooled rapidly to form rocks that had mostly a pumice structure or a glassy obsidian structure, any associated gases escaping into the atmosphere before the mass solidified.

The plutonic rocks were formed deep down below the surface where the molten matter solidified much more slowly; most of the gases were retained, and a definite crystalline structure, which differed greatly from that of pumice and obsidian, developed. These plutonic rocks are commonly known as granites. And such granitic rock constitutes a substantial base beneath all the other kinds of rocks that are found on or near the surface of Earth.

Granite makes up a large part of the interiors of many mountains. These mountains may have been formed by a tremendous upheaval of granite from deep down in the interior of Earth. Or molten rock from which granite was subsequently formed may have moved upward to fill in the rock voids after some gigantic force had shoved the surface rocks to a much greater height than they originally occupied.

Since granite is formed far below the surface rather than near or on it, some type of drastic erosion had to operate before the granite came into view. But time, in billions of years, was at Earth's disposal. And such erosive forces as heat and cold, wind and water, and sand and ice have operated over long periods of time to remove the overlying burdens of volcanic and sedimentary rocks to expose large expanses of granite.

The word granite is here employed to cover all forms of plutonic rocks, whether they are true granites as defined by the geologist and mineralogist or not. But about 90 per cent of the plutonic rocks are true granites. And the term granite has come to stand for something very substantial. Thus the Dartmouth College song says of its students: "They have the still north in their hearts, the hill winds in their veins, and the granite of New Hampshire in their muscles and their brains." New Hampshire is known as the "Granite State," a great deal of this kind of rock being exposed or being readily within reach by quarrying inside its borders.

Large masses of granite are now open to view in many parts of Earth. Stone Mountain, Georgia, is a mass of granite seven hundred feet high and seven miles in circumference, on the face of which a giant figure of Jefferson Davis, president of the southern Confederacy, has been hewn. An exposure of granite extends from the Canadian border northward into Alaska for a distance of 1,100 miles and a width of 80 to 120 miles. In the southeastern part of Ireland is a mass of granite seven hundred miles in length and between seven to seventeen miles in width. Aberdeen, Scotland is known as the "Granite City."

Huge granite boulders, derived from plutonic rocks in Canada that were uncovered and broken up by the glaciers of the Ice Age, are widely scattered about over the northern part of the United States along the southern terminal of the glacial advance line extending from Long Island, New York across Pennsylvania into southern Ohio and on northwestward across Indiana, Illinois, Missouri, and Iowa to Nebraska, the Dakotas, and Montana.

The word granite is derived from the Latin *granum,* meaning "grain." This refers to the visible crystalline structure of granite and to the manner in which the mineral crystals are fitted together in the rock. These crystals, forming slowly, grew into well-defined forms that are characteristic of the several minerals. They can usually be identified without the use of a magnifying glass, especially from a freshly broken surface.

Four types of minerals make up the largest part of every piece of granite. Usually about 60 per cent of granite is orthoclase or some quite similar mineral, 30 per cent is quartz, and the remaining 10 per cent is made up of darker-colored minerals of which biotite and hornblende are examples. Granite is usually flesh-colored, but it may also be white with black crystals intermingled.

The dark minerals crystallized first. Being still surrounded by molten matter and, in fact, dissolved in it, they were free to grow into beautiful crystalline forms. The orthoclase then began to crystallize, but under somewhat more constricted conditions, so the crystals are not quite so perfect. Finally, the quartz crystallized into whatever space remained in the now nearly solid rock. Its crystals, therefore, were much more irregular in form, developing into an interlocking arrangement with the other mineral crystals. This gave the granite not only its granular structure but the rigidity and toughness for which it is noted.

The many varieties of granite differ greatly, depending on the differences in nature of the molten material from which they were formed. Also, there are many other closely related kinds of plutonic rocks. And the volcanic rocks that were formed under more rapid cooling on the surface of Earth are quite similar in make-up to the granites. They may, however, contain more of some elements and less of others, and they generally exist in noncrystalline form, although mineral crystals have been formed in some of them.

Granite, the typical example of plutonic igneous rock, is well suited for illustrating what happens when such rocks disintegrate to form soil. It represents the starting point for the vast deposits of sandstone, limestone, and shale that cover the larger part of the land surface, for all the soil that was derived from these rocks and now lies as a mantle on top of them, and for all the salts and sediment in the sea. And granite forms the solid base on which everything on the surface of Earth is located.

Quartz, one of the most important mineral components of granite, consists of silicon and oxygen joined to each other. These two elements, one a solid and the other a gas in their elemental states, are tightly bound together in definite crystalline form. Quartz is a hard mineral, virtually insoluble in water. When granite goes to pieces to form soil, the quartz grains remain mostly as such, in very hard particles of sand that give the soil a gritty feel. Opal, jasper, agate, chalcedony, and flint are highly attractive forms of nearly pure quartz.

The sizes of the quartz particles in soils depend on the extent to which the original crystals have been mechanically broken into smaller pieces and the degree to which they have been abraded by being rubbed against each other or against other particles of rock. Much of the sand on beaches and in sand dunes consists of grains of quartz that were weathered from granite during remote geological time. Much finer particles of quartz are found in soils of the glaciated areas where massive quantities of granite and other rocks were carried southward in the slowly moving ice. There a great deal of the quartz and much of all the other minerals was ground into a fine flour as the icebound rock, weighed down by great masses of ice on top, was shoved across the denuded layers of rock beneath.

Orthoclase also contains silicon and oxygen. But in this case they are joined to two other elements—potassium and aluminum—to form a very different kind of mineral, a silicate. This silicate was much more susceptible to attack by water than was quartz. And the solubilizing effects of water were materially increased by the presence in it of carbonic acid that came down dissolved in the water as it fell from the sky as rain. This water also contained some active nitric acid that had been formed as a result of lightning discharges in the atmosphere. And when the rain reached the soil it picked up additional acid, such as the sulphuric acid that is formed during the breakdown of mineral sulfides in certain types of rock. Pyrites, from which large amounts of sulfuric acid have been and are being made by factory procedures, is a good example of such a mineral sulfide.

As a result of this dissolving process, the rate of which increased with the amount of mineral surface exposed by disintegration of the rock, the orthoclase was robbed of most of its potassium, which was carried away in solution in the drainage water and dumped into the sea. The part that remained of the orthoclase went to pieces to form the finely divided clay, the material that gives soil its sticky feel. And large amounts of this clay, a virtually insoluble substance, were carried out to sea in suspension. In due time this suspended clay fell to the bottom of the sea where it built up into deposits that later were solidified to form shale.

Biotite, a still more complex mineral silicate, contains not only the elements that go into the making of orthoclase but some additional magnesium and iron as well. A much softer mineral than orthoclase, it is much more readily reduced to clay, with loss not only of its potassium in the drainage water but of its magnesium as well. Most of its iron remained behind as a constituent of the clay that was either carried out to sea in suspension or became a part of the soil that was formed.

Hornblende, another complex mineral silicate, contains calcium and magnesium in place of the potassium that is found in orthoclase, and iron instead of aluminum. In breaking down to form soil it yielded a somewhat different type of clay as it released most of its calcium and magnesium to the drainage water and to the sea. It was this calcium and magnesium, plus that released in the breakdown of other similar silicate minerals, that was joined to the air-derived carbonic acid in sea water to form the vast deposits of calcium and magnesium carbonates that were laid down in the deep sea and later consolidated into limestone rock.

Starting with granite and related igneous rocks, the end point was soil, consisting of coarse quartz-sand particles, finely divided silicate-derived clay particles, and intermediate-sized silt particles of variable make-up, plus the soluble salts. Some of the sand, silt, and clay and most of the dissolved materials were carried out to sea. That which remained as soil was virtually insoluble and essentially indestructible.

Small quantities of a great variety of other minerals are found in granite and related rocks. Some of these closely resemble those already described, but others are quite different. Among these others are apatite, a carrier of phosphorus; pyrite, a compound of iron and sulfur; pyrolusite, a source of manganese; and tourmaline, the source of most of the boron in soils and in plants growing in them. All of the soil-derived elements required by plants, animals, and man, and many others, are found in mineral forms in granite and other igneous rocks.

The larger part of the supplies of these mineral nutrients was dissolved out of the rock and its residues during the soil-forming process and lost to the sea. But enough remained attached to the fine clay particles to meet the needs of the plants that ultimately came into being and covered the soil. And as these original plants grew up, matured, died, and fell back on the land, they returned the borrowed mineral nutrients to the soil from which they had come. This returned portion was in a more readily usable state for new growths of plants than that still contained in the clay.

Many precious minerals are found in granite, including garnet, jade, topaz, and zircon. A great variety of ores are found associated with granitic rocks, including those that yield uranium, gold, silver, copper, lead, tin, zinc, and mercury. One wonders whether plants grown on the soil derived from rocks containing more than normal quantities of these precious elements have any special nutritive values. On the other hand, it is known that some of the rarer mineral elements found in rocks have injurious effects, at least when present in relatively large amounts, as in the case of molybdenum, selenium and fluorine.

Crystal forms of carbon, called diamonds, are being mined in a few widely scattered locations, the most important deposits of these gems being found in South Africa. These diamonds occur in volcanic extrusions through carbon-containing substances, the lava apparently serving as a solvent for the carbon compounds from which the carbon separates out in crystalline form. Diamonds for industrial purposes are being made artificially by embedding charcoal in molten iron and then suddenly chilling the mixture.

More than 90 per cent of the substance in igneous rocks, including the granites, is made up of eight of the somewhat over one hundred elements of which all matter—that of the land, the sea, and the atmosphere—is made. Of these eight, silicon and oxygen constitute about 74 per cent; iron, aluminum, and titanium about 13 per cent; and calcium, magnesium, sodium, and potassium, in the order named, about 11 per cent. The remaining 2 per cent is made up of such elements as phosphorus and sulfur, both highly essential to the well-being of all living things; the equally necessary cobalt, copper, zinc, manganese, molybdenum, and iodine, which are classified as trace elements; and still smaller quantities of a greater variety of other elements of little or no known value to plants, animals, or man.

For the purposes of this book, an element can best be defined by examples. Gold, silver, copper, and iron are metallic elements. Calcium, magnesium, sodium, and potassium, all silvery solids, belong to an alkaline group of elements. Hydrogen, nitrogen, chlorine, and fluorine, all gases, are examples of an acid-forming group. Oxygen, a gas, and silicon and aluminum, both solids, when joined together constitute the major part of the soil. And hydrogen and oxygen, both gases, are joined to form water. Some of these elements are found in an elemental state in nature. Others can readily be reduced to that state. But, for the most part, the many elements exist in combinations of two or more that are known as compounds. All of the mineral compounds are solids.

Rocks and soils contain virtually no elements as such. They are made up of combinations of mineral-forming elements in a great variety of crystal forms, some in very large quantities and others in much lesser amounts. The salts of the sea are likewise compounds of various elements dissolved in water from which they can readily be recovered by evaporation of the water. The lime deposit in the bottom of the country teakettle is such a salt. But the most common of the salts that remain dissolved in sea water is sodium chloride, a combination of solid sodium and gaseous chlorine. Plants are made up mostly of organic compounds that were formed by joining the water that fell as rain with the carbon dioxide and nitrogen gases of the atmosphere. Less than 5 per cent of the average plant is soil-derived mineral matter.

The nature of the climate, rather than that of the underlying rock, largely determined the kind of soil that was formed in any given region. Under any specific set of climatic conditions the soil is essentially the same at maturity no matter what the nature of the rock from which it was formed. Granite and limestone, for example, are very different kinds of rock. Granite is an igneous rock, it is hard, and it is made up mostly of quartz, orthoclase, biotite, and hornblende. Limestone is a sedimentary rock, it is relatively soft, and it is made up mostly of carbonates of calcium and magnesium. Selecting conditions such as those that obtain in New England and allowing sufficient time for the soil to reach maturity, one can expect a gray-brown soil with acid characteristics, whatever the underlying rock may be.

At the start of the soil-forming process something over 80 per cent of the granite would have been silicon, aluminum, and iron and the oxygen that is associated with them. But limestone usually contains less than 10 per cent of these three mineral elements and their associated oxygen. The remaining 90 per cent or more of the limestone consists of calcium and magnesium joined to carbon and oxygen. Only the impurities of the limestone remain behind to form soil. And these impurities are nothing more or less than sand, silt, and clay that developed during the breakdown of the earlier granitic rocks. These impurities had become entangled with the calcium and magnesium carbonates as they separated out of the sea water and fell to the ocean floor, the first step in limestone formation.

The quantities of rock required for the formation of a one-foot depth of soil over a unit area would have been quite different for granite and for limestone. A very large part of the granite would have remained as sand and clay to constitute the soil. But most of the limestone would have disappeared. Thus if the impurities in the limestone had totaled 5 per cent, a depth of at least twenty feet of limestone would have been required to yield one foot of soil. Much of the limestone is considerably purer than that.

In the earlier stages of development of soil from these two classes of rock, that being formed from granite would have been much better for crop-growing puposes. It would have contained a much greater wealth of most of the nutrients required by plants and animals. Gradually, however, under New England conditions it would have become a strongly acid soil, as the alkaline elements were leached out and carried off in the drainage water. At this point the soil of limestone origin would have had the advantage. It, too, might have become acid on the surface. But fragments of limestone would still have remained in the subsoil. And the subsoil would be lying on top of possibly very deep layers of limestone that had not yet been disintegrated to form soil. This limestone would still be within the reach of the roots of plants and these roots would grow down into the cracks, absorbing lime from the sides of them. This lime would be transported to the tops of the plants and some of it would be left behind in the soil in the form of plant residues from which it would later be released by microbial action.

In the hot and humid tropics the disintegration of rock to form soil often goes much farther than in the humid temperate regions with the result that the clay loses its silica and is reduced to iron and aluminum oxides. The ultimate product, called a laterite, is really not a soil but a consolidated product that can be used for building purposes. Under these conditions so little of the necessary mineral nutrients remains, except for the iron itself, and the physical properties of the product are so unsatisfactory for the growth of plant roots that little can be done toward using the land for crop production.

Such complete disintegration of the original rocks is effected only over long periods of time and only under the most drastic climatic conditions in relation to the action of the atmospheric elements on the rock and soil. With increasing distance from the centers of formation of laterite and with less complete breakdown of the clay, forests grow in great profusion where rainfall is adequate. But once the forest is removed and the land is farmed, the lasting qualities of the soil, in terms of fertility, are limited. This land will grow a good crop for a few years after the forest growth has been cut down and left lying on the land and its mineral nutrients have been released by microbial action. The usual cropping system in such a region is one in which the land is permitted to return to forests every few years during which period new supplies of mineral nutrients are collected from the soil and underlying rock.

Returning to the original granite, not only is there something very substantial about this rock but about the soil derived directly from it. Most of our soil is derived from sedimentary rocks that, much earlier, were derived from granite and similar igneous rock. But soil originating in fresh granite itself is credited with being a "strong" soil. Those people who were born in areas of granite-derived soil seem to have absorbed some of its sturdy characteristics. Those who were born in regions where the glaciers dropped their loads of granite boulders and the flour into which many of them had been ground, have likewise benefited from the granite. These rocks and their products brought new life to a vast area of land in the northern parts of North America, and to northern Europe as well. And wind and water carried large quantities of granite particles and flour long distances farther south to become a part of the soil.

Finally, there is something comforting in the knowledge that all the land on which we live is firmly located on a solid granite base. Even though this granite is far below the surface in most locations and well-covered with deep layers of sedimentary rocks and soil derived from them, it is there. Only such titanic forces as those associated with earthquakes can break through it and even then only superficially, for granite and closely related solid igneous rock extend downward a distance of some eighteen hundred miles below the surface.

And he stooped sometimes and gathered some of the earth up in his hand and he sat and held it thus, and it seemed full of life between his fingers. And he was content, holding it thus.

—PEARL BUCK IN *The Good Earth*

Chapter Five

LIFE WITHIN THE SOIL

AN APPLE, a blade of grass, a cornstalk, or even a mighty oak that falls to the ground soon disappears. And the same applies to the body of a bird, a beast, a mouse, or a man, once it is buried in the soil. Myriads of microbes, so small they cannot be seen except by the aid of a microscope, are standing by waiting to digest whatever may come their way in the form of once living but now lifeless matter. What a wilderness of plant and animal refuse this world would be without these highly active but unseen forms of life that inhabit the soil! And when these microbes themselves die, their dead bodies likewise disappear. Whatever their kind or size, all living things come into existence, grow, reproduce, die, and then are reduced to the gaseous, liquid, and mineral components of which they were made. These components are the carbon dioxide and nitrogen gases of the atmosphere, the water that falls as rain, and the ash elements that are contributed by the soil.

One acre, or 43,560 square feet, of soil to a plow depth of seven inches weighs about two million pounds. One pound is equivalent to nearly 454 grams. One gram of good soil may contain as many as one billion microbes. The numbers of these microbes in an acre, a pound, or a gram of soil at any given time and place depends on the quantity and nature of the plant and animal refuse in the soil, on the air and moisture relationships in the soil, and on the temperature of the soil. Their numbers fluctuate widely during the course of any one year, and often within a period as short as a day. Under the most favorable circumstances the total weight of living microbes in a plowed acre of soil might well be six thousand pounds. Of this living weight possibly five thousand pounds would be water that could be driven off into the air in a drying oven at 100°C. The remaining one thousand pounds would be dry matter. If this dry matter were burned, probably fifty pounds of ashes would remain. And these ashes would represent the contribution that had been made by the mineral substance of the soil, directly or indirectly, to the microbes themselves. In other words, the mineral elements of the soil are just as essential to a microbe as they are to a larger plant, an animal, or a man.

Soil microbes perform a great variety of very useful functions. They serve first as scavengers, getting rid of what otherwise would be troublesome accumulations of dead plants and animals. But they also serve as agents for keeping the several required constituents of plants in circulation by way of air, water, and soil for repeated use in perpetuity. These constituents must be used over and over again in nature's economy. To trace the history of any one molecule of carbon dioxide, nitrogen, or water over all time since life began would be an impossible undertaking. Suffice it to say that a given atom of carbon-dioxide-derived carbon now contained in the body of a given living plant or animal may have been in the body of the first living microbe, the body of a prehistoric animal, and the bodies of many intervening and subsequent generations of plants, animals, and men. The carbon dioxide from which this carbon came was in the original atmosphere and it has escaped and will re-escape back into the atmosphere again and again with the passing of time. There must always be carbon dioxide in the atmosphere, otherwise plants cannot exist, and neither can man.

Soil organic matter, whatever its origin, is the day-to-day food of soil microorganisms. This organic matter, being largely the refuse of plants, is made up mostly of sugars, starches, cellulose, lignins, oils, and proteins, intermingled with the ash elements that were derived from the soil. Any animal bodies that may be present in the soil will be made up mostly of proteins, fats, and ash elements. The fats of animals are closely related to the oils of plants. And when the microbes have digested this organic matter it will have been changed to carbon dioxide, nitrate, water, and ash.

Except for its protein and mineral matter, most of the soil organic matter is made up of carbon, hydrogen, and oxygen—all derived from the carbon dioxide gas that was breathed in through the leaves of plants and from the water that was absorbed by their roots. Proteins, however, contain not only carbon, hydrogen, and oxygen, but nitrogen as well. Most of the nitrogen of Earth exists as a gas in the atmosphere. But only the legumes, of which the several clovers are examples, can make use of this atmospheric nitrogen. They do this by way of the bacteria living in the small nodules that are attached to their roots.

The nonlegume plants obtain their nitrogen from the soil in the form of a nitrate produced by a specific group of microbes that are able to manufacture this substance out of proteins. This nitrate might well be calcium nitrate or nitrate of lime—a beautiful white crystalline salt when purified, but which exists in the soil only in its dissolved form in water. This nitrate is produced microbially in three steps and by three groups of microorganisms: the first releases ammonia from the protein, the second changes the ammonia to a nitrite, and the third completes the process with the production of a nitrate.

One of the outstanding aspects of the nitrogen problem as applied to the nutrition of plants is the close relationship that exists between the specific group of microbes, the nodule-producing bacteria, and the specific group of plants, the legumes. The nodules these bacteria produce are attached to the roots of the legumes. They vary greatly in size and shape, some of them being about the size of a grape seed, others resembling peas in size and shape, and still others existing in clusters as large as walnuts. Within these nodules the microbes live and carry on their function of taking nitrogen gas from the soil air and transforming it into products out of which protein can be made. The microbes and the legumes live in a symbiotic relationship, the legumes contributing the foods other than nitrogen that the microbes require and the microbes contributing the nitrogen products the legumes require.

The legume family of higher plants includes not only the clovers but beans, peas, peanuts, soybeans, alfalfa, and a great variety of other crop plants that are highly useful for feed and food purposes. It also includes a number of trees, such as the mesquite of semiarid regions, the locust and acacia trees of the humid temperate regions, and the mahogany and ebony trees of the high-rainfall tropics. When these legume plants fall to the ground, whether in part or in whole, the protein they contain that was microbially synthesized out of the gaseous nitrogen of the air, is released to the soil for action of the microbes that change protein nitrogen to nitrate.

The fertility value of legumes was known by the Romans long before the time of Christ. But the explanation of their soil-improving properties was not discovered until 1886, when it was demonstrated by German chemists and microbiologists that the bacteria in the nodules on the roots were the responsible agents. Subsequently, some of the nodule bacteria were isolated, studied under the microscope, and named *Rhizobium*. There are a great many different strains of these club-shaped bacteria. For example, those living in the nodules on the roots of peas are not the same as those in the nodules on the roots of beans and alfalfa. And they cannot be substituted for each other on these legumes.

When the legume dies the nodules are digested by soil microbes, but the nodule bacteria are released into the soil unharmed, where they await the coming of a new planting of that legume. Shortly after the seed of the legume germinate and the young seedlings get underway, the nitrogen-fixing bacteria attach themselves to the roots, and new nodules begin to form. At this point the young plants turn dark green and grow with increased vigor. In proportion as these nodules grow in size and number, the legume benefits to an ever greater degree from the more abundant supply of air-derived nitrogen that has been put at its disposal by the nodule bacteria. And the legume grows ever more luxuriantly with darker-green leaves, assuming that all its other nutrient needs have been met.

When introducing a new legume to any location, it was once the practice to obtain soil from a field in which that legume had been grown successfully, as a means of carrying over a large enough number of the right kind of nodule bacteria to be sure that the roots of the new plants would quickly be inoculated. Sometimes a sufficient number of the nodule bacteria were present in the dust on the seed to meet the requirements. But this soil dust could not always be depended on to supply the needed nitrogen-fixing microbes.

Such procedures are no longer depended on or employed. In fact, such superior strains of nodule bacteria have been developed by careful selection from within the nodules on the roots of luxuriantly growing legume plants that virtually all legume seed are now inoculated with pure cultures of these strains. This applies whether the specific legume has ever been grown on the field in question or not. And a different legume culture is used for each legume, this culture having been developed from the microbes in nodules on the roots of that species of legume. The rhizobia for these cultures are taken from these nodules under aseptic conditions, put in liquid media containing sugar and mineral nutrients, grown to rapid multiplication of numbers under optimum temperature and aeration conditions, and then sprinkled over the seed in this liquid suspension form or changed into dust form by being poured over some type of pulverized solid medium such as sterilized peat.

A good bit of work has been done in an effort to get the nodule bacteria to produce nodules on the roots of nonlegume crop plants, notably corn. The method of procedure was to grow the rhizobia in liquid cultures, such as are now employed in preparing cultures for sale for inoculating purposes. The difference in this case was that extracts from corn plants were introduced into the liquid cultures to get the microbes adjusted to the juices of this non-legume plant species. The proportion of the extract from the corn plants in relation to that of the normal culture medium was gradually increased. The microbes appeared to thrive in this new culture solution. But when the corn seed were inoculated with it, no nodules ever developed on the roots of the plants grown from this seed.

For a long time it was believed that the fixation of gaseous nitrogen by legumes was accomplished by way of their leaves, notwithstanding that the rhizobia lived in the nodules on their roots. Careful tests were made with plants that were grown in sand, the roots being enclosed in sealed containers. All the air in the containers was replaced by a mixture of pure oxygen and carbon dioxide. This meant that no nitrogen gas was in contact with the roots of the plants, although there was an abundance of nitrogen in the natural air around their leaves. But no fixation of nitrogen occurred. Evidently, the nitrogen that is fixed by the nodule bacteria is that in the soil air and not that in the atmosphere surrounding the leaves.

A number of free-living types of bacteria that do not live in symbiosis with legumes or any other higher plants have been discovered. Of these, the *Azotobacter* is the most effective. These microbes feed on the soil organic matter, particularly on the types that are high in sugars, starches, and celluloses and low in proteins, such as wheat straw and cornstalks. Under optimum conditions in the laboratory, which involve temperatures around 80°F. and adequate but not excessive supplies of moisture, together with suitable amounts of sugar and mineral nutrients, the azotobacter naturally present in good soil are capable of fixing considerable amounts of air nitrogen. Calculated from dish cultures to an acre basis, the quantity of nitrogen so fixed may be considerably greater than that fixed by the legume plants on an acre of land. In the case of legumes the fixed nitrogen is stored in protein form both in the bodies of the nodule bacteria and in the legume plants.

With azotobacter the storage is in the microbes themselves from which it is later released in nitrate form when they die and their bodies are digested by other microbes.

The quantity of nitrogen that is changed from the gaseous to the combined protein form by rhizobia and azotobacter depends in large degree on the quantity of nitrate being produced by the microbial population in the soil from that already stored in the soil organic matter. Like all other forms of life, these nitrogen-fixing bacteria take the easiest path, and that is to use the already manufactured nitrate. Consequently, if the soil is already supplied with organic matter, has been liberally treated with well-rotted manure, or has received a liberal application of a nitrogen-carrying fertilizer, particularly a nitrate, little nitrogen fixation occurs.

The plow depth of an average acre of soil contains around 60,000 pounds of organic matter on an ovendry basis. In this there is about 3,000 pounds of nitrogen, mostly in protein form. It is on this nitrogen that most crops depend. Accordingly, active bacterial release of this nitrogen in nitrate form is essential. As the temperature rises in the spring, the winter-dormant soil microbes awake and set to work in earnest. As a result, nitrate to the extent of possibly 150 pounds of nitrogen an acre will be released for crop use during the growing season. If the crop, grown to its full potential, requires more nitrate nitrogen than this, it will have to be supplied in fertilizer form.

One acre of good land located in a humid temperate region will produce about 10,000 pounds dry weight of alfalfa hay each year. This will contain about 250 pounds of nitrogen, and the roots of the alfalfa may contain another 50 pounds of this element. Under average conditions possibly one-half of this nitrogen would come from the nitrate that was released by microbial action on the soil organic matter and the other half would be obtained from the nitrogen gas in the soil air by way of the nodule bacteria on the roots.

About 20 per cent of the nitrogen in any feed that is consumed by animals goes to market as meat, eggs, milk, or wool, the other 80 per cent being excreted by the animals in the urine and feces. These manurial substances can be returned to the field. The same applies to the food eaten by man, except that in this case the point of consumption is normally far removed from the farm where the foodstuff was produced. Furthermore, most of the excreta of European and American city people is lost by way of sewage disposal systems. In some countries, notably in China, Korea, and Japan, it is saved and returned to the soil. In any event, most of the nitrogen losses must be compensated for by growing legumes and encouraging the azotobacter, or they must be made good by the use of nitrogen fertilizers.

There is abundant evidence, however, that some of the blue-green algae, minute forms of plant life that grow in soils under conditions of a relatively high supply of moisture, obtain much of their nitrogen from the air. The manner in which this is accomplished is not known. These algae make important contributions to the nitrogen supplies of paddy rice. No doubt they function on upland soils in like manner during the warmer and moister parts of the year. They may fix nitrogen more or less continuously in the warmer and wetter tropical forest lands.

One of the most intriguing phenomena of nature is the large deposit of nitrate in Chile. When water containing nitrate is evaporated to dryness it leaves its nitrate as a residue that resembles common salt. If the water containing the nitrate had been collected as drainage from an ordinary soil, this would be nitrate of lime. In Chile, however, it is nitrate of soda. Many millions of tons of Chilean nitrate of soda have been mined, refined, and marketed the world over, and much more remains to be exploited.

Some scientists believe that these nitrate deposits had their origin in microbial action on the large quantities of guano left behind over long periods of time by the millions of birds that have fished off the shores of Chile, living and dying on the nearby land. Continued rapid rotting of this guano and the dead bodies of these birds under the highly favorable climatic conditions of the coastal highlands should have led to the bacterial production of large quantities of nitrates over the millions of years that have passed since this land was stabilized. Dissolved in rain water, this nitrate might well have been carried downward through the underlying soil and rock to a lower-lying water table. From there it might well have been carried, by way of underground water channels, beneath the nearby flat desert where the water, moving upward to and evaporating from the surface, left its load of nitrate behind, in this case mostly as nitrate of soda.

Notwithstanding the large tonnages of nitrate of soda still available for use by agriculture from the Chilean deposits, the quantities processed have long been far from adequate to meet all the needs for increased crop production. And even though the rhizobia of legumes and the azotobacter are highly efficient fixers of atmospheric nitrogen, they are inadequate sources of the extra nitrogen required. Consequently, a great deal of research effort has gone into the development of techniques by which atmospheric nitrogen can be changed to ammonia and nitrate by factory procedures. As a result we now have a large number of nitrogen-fixing factories scattered about over Earth. Total world consumption of fertilizer nitrogen amounted to around seven million metric tons in 1958. This is equivalent to forty million tons of nitrate of soda. But most of the factory-fixed nitrogen is now being supplied in other more concentrated forms, such as anhydrous ammonia, urea, and ammonium nitrate. The first is a gas that can be compressed to a clear liquid and put directly into the soil where it is absorbed by the soil and held for plant use. The last two are attractive white salts resembling sugar; they dissolve readily in water and are immediately available for plant use, once they have been applied to the soil.

Although the production of nitrate from the plant and animal protein substances is a highly important function of the microorganisms that bring about the decomposition of soil organic matter, their release of the other plant nutrients from this organic matter is equally important. Each plant has within it all the nutrients needed by another plant of the same size and kind. If one could afford it, an excellent way to build up the production capacity of a soil would be to grow and plow under successive crops, particularly legumes. Each of these crops would be able to feed on the nutrients released by microbial action on the previous crop. Each time round the cycle some extra nitrogen would be accumulated by the nodule bacteria or the azotobacter. Likewise, each time round additional quantities of the natural supplies of mineral nutrients in the soil would be released for crop use. Usually, however, the crop must be harvested and sold, so dependence has to be placed on crop refuse, manures, and cover crops for supplying organic matter to feed the soil microbes.

Fertilizers have great supplemental value in developing adequate supplies of soil organic matter. Higher acre yields can be produced by their use and these higher yields leave more crop residues in and on the soil. Microbial digestion of this soil organic matter releases its constituents back to both air and soil. But complete destruction of this organic matter is never accomplished, some of the more resistant portions, the lignins, remaining behind in the soil in virtually indestructible form, save by fire. And these lignins serve a highly useful purpose in maintaining good working quality in the soil. To have a live soil, however, it is necessary to continue to feed the soil microbes fresh plant and animal refuse, reinforced with extra supplies of all the mineral nutrients needed both by the crop plants and by the soil microbes that digest their refuse.

Some microbes can be as destructive to higher forms of life as others are useful to them. Many of them are parasites that fasten themselves to their plant and animal hosts. Some of our most troublesome plant diseases, such as the blights, rusts, and smuts, are caused by microbes. Many of these microbes harbor in the soil awaiting an opportunity to attack their hosts. But many of the microorganisms that are responsible for human and animal diseases cannot survive in the soil. Such disease-controlling substances as penicillin and streptomycin are products of microorganisms that live in the soil and that have been isolated from the soil.

In the production of antibiotics, specific microbes known to produce such substances are isolated and grown in pure cultures in a specially developed liquid medium. Only very small quantities of the antibiotic are produced by these microorganisms per gallon of solution. Accordingly, large gallonages of the solution must be prepared, sterilized, inoculated with the pure culture, incubated, and processed to obtain the large amounts of the purified powdered antibiotic that are now being used for remedial purposes.

Most of the microbes that are being used for industrial production of antibiotics have been isolated from the soil. They were first identified on microbial culture plates where the antibiotic substance spread out around the individual colonies of the antibiotic-producing microbes and destroyed nearby colonies of other microbes. A great variety of such antibiotics are now being produced. Some of them are so toxic to living things that they cannot be used as curative agents against microbial diseases of animals and man. Other milder antibiotics are being added to livestock and poultry feeds as preventives of microbial diseases. The results of their use are often quite spectacular, notably during the earlier stages of growth of the animals. Still other antibiotics are being employed to good effect in sprays as a means of curing certain microbial diseases of plants.

Pure cultures of certain disease-producing microbes are being used in the control of certain insects. The "milky disease" of Japanese beetles is a good example. In this case the microbes that produce the disease are grown in pure culture on a large scale and then applied to the soil where they lie in wait to attack the larval forms of the insects before they emerge from the soil as beetles. The spreading of the milky disease is accomplished by way of the beetles themselves before they have succumbed and through the droppings of birds that consume the larval grubs.

Higher orders of plants, such as the tomato, also produce antibioticlike substances that aid in protecting themselves against disease. One wonders, for example, how it is that plant roots grow down into the soil without harm from the millions of millions of microbes that surround them. As long as the roots remain alive, they are not generally attacked, although there are some troublesome exceptions. But as soon as a plant comes to maturity and dies, the microbes set to work to digest its dead roots.

There are, of course, many microbial diseases of live plants, some affecting the roots and others the tops. Some of these diseases are carried over from one plant generation to the next by way of the soil, some by way of the seed, and some by way of the wind. The point being made here, however, is that plants have a certain capacity to ward off disease-producing microbes, some species and varieties much more so than others. A great deal of work has been and is being done to breed and select plants for disease resistance, and some remarkable developments have occurred in this field of study.

Many microbes are closely associated with the outsides of roots where they apparently benefit from the excretions of these roots and, in return, make the mineral nutrients in the soil immediately surrounding the roots more available to the plant. This is another symbiotic relationship quite similar to that between the nodule bacteria and the legumes. Some of the root-associated microbes, such as the mycorrhizal fungi, actually penetrate the surface cells of the roots and develop inside them to greater benefit to themselves and to the associated plant as well. This particular group of microbes appears to be of special importance in getting tree seedlings under way, particularly under conditions of low soil fertility.

One of the most troublesome of the disease-producing types of root-inhabiting microbes is the nematode. In contrast to most of the microbes previously mentioned, the nematode is a microscopic animal rather than a microscopic plant. It attacks the roots of a great many plants, particularly in the warmer and more humid regions of Earth. Large knots, bearing some resemblance to the nodules on the roots of legumes but being much less attractive and far more extended, cover the roots of affected plants. Coming into prominence only recently, this field of study is a challenge to research workers.

The skins of animals, like the outer tissues of plants, are also highly resistant to attacks of microbes. The man who works about the farm, yard, or garden is constantly getting soil on his hands. And this soil is the place where many disease organisms affecting not only plants but animals and man find a resting place. The dust that is always present in the atmosphere and comes to rest on the soil is also a carrier of a great variety of microbes. Yet nothing much seems to happen from daily contact with soil so contaminated. Sometimes microbes gain entrance to an animal or a man by way of a wound, as in the case of soil-borne tetanus. And some diseases, such as typhoid fever, attack man by way of his alimentary tract. It would appear that the linings of the openings to the body are more susceptible to attacks of microbial disease organisms than are the skin tissues.

Where did these microbes originate? Their ancestors, no doubt, were the first living things on Earth. When Earth cooled down and conditions became favorable for life, it came into being. And this first form of life must have been a simple one-celled microbe that eventually developed the capacity to cut itself in half to form two one-celled microbes. Conceivably, the first microbes were preceded by still simpler forms, such as the viruses that appear to be about half way between the animate and inanimate. There was no organic matter on which these first microbes could feed since that was long before the larger plants, which have been the primary source of the soil organic matter, had come into existence. So these original microbes had to manufacture their own organic matter out of purely inorganic substances. The raw materials for this were water, rock refuse, the gases of the atmosphere, and the salts of the sea.

When the first microbe succeeded in dividing itself into two microbes, the principle of reproduction began to operate. From this point on increase in bacterial numbers may have been quite rapid. Many microbes now reach maturity and divide within thirty minutes or less. At that rate of reproduction a single microbe could grow into 300 million microbes in twenty-four hours. If nothing prevented continuance of this reproductive process, all the seas on Earth would be overflowing with microbes within a short period of time.

But the principle of death came into play. Competition for living space and for food brought about an equilibrium at which reproduction and death came into balance. The number of microbes increased with each new improvement in living conditions and each increase in food supplies, and it fell back whenever living conditions deteriorated and the supplies of food had been largely exhausted. Some of the microbes were able to survive long periods in a resting stage without need of food.

In this struggle for existence, some microbes found it much simpler to feed on the dead bodies of their fellows than to continue synthesizing new supplies of food from purely inorganic materials. Others managed to attach themselves as parasites to other living microbes, which may be said to have served as unwilling hosts. But with the advent of higher plants and animals and more abundant supplies of already synthesized products in their refuse, the microbes adjusted themselves to this more readily usable supply of food. In due time the principle of dynamic equilibrium came to apply, and to an ever greater degree. With each new input of organic matter into the soil the number of microbes rapidly increased. As this organic matter was consumed, many of the microbes died of starvation. At one time the number would be rapidly increasing and at another rapidly decreasing.

Eventually, the total amount of work to be done in the soil by the microbial population that had evolved was divided up among the microbes. Some collected nitrogen from the air. Some served as scavengers. Some released ammonia from protein substances. Some changed this ammonia to nitrite and to nitrate. A great variety of other kinds of work had to be done.

Eventually, the number of different kinds of microbes and the number of very different things they did became legion. Meanwhile the principle of evolution had come into play. Microorganisms themselves not only evolved into new types, including bacteria, fungi, yeasts, and actinomycetes, but they became differentiated into plants and animals. Included among the animal forms were the protozoa, many species of which exist in soils.

From these humble beginnings still more complex and much larger forms of plant and animal life evolved. Starting with the simpler marine plants, the ferns, flowering plants, shrubs, and trees came successively into being and occupied the land. In the animal line the protozoa were eventually followed by insects on the land and in the air and by the fishes in the sea. In due time the mammals, birds, and apes evolved. Finally, the forerunners of man entered the picture something over a million years ago.

But microbes did not go out of existence. The number of species continued to increase. The soil harbors far more of these many species than any other medium. It is difficult now to conceive of Earth or soil without microbes. They were here many millions of years before man arrived and they, no doubt, will still be here when he disappears from Earth. Some of them are essential to his existence; others are of little known value. And still others are harmful, if not to man himself, then by their attacks on the plants and animals on which he depends for food and fiber. Conceivably, new life is still originating from purely inorganic substances to add to the microbial population of the soil.

All seasons and their changes, all please alike;
Sweet is the breath of morn, her rising sweet
With charm of earliest birds; pleasant the sun
When first on this delightful land he spreads
His orient beams on herb, tree, fruit, and flower
Glist'ning with dew; fragrant the fertile earth
After soft showers; and sweet the coming on
Of grateful ev'ning mild, then silent night.

—JOHN MILTON

Chapter Six
THE BREATH OF LIFE

AIR is the breath of life. It may be so calm as not even to stir the leaves of trees. It may be so turbulent as to pull these trees up by their roots. It may manifest itself as a gentle breeze, a brisk wind, a tornado, a hurricane, or a typhoon. One cannot see the air, sometimes cannot even feel it. But one is aware that it is there. And without it no life can exist.

Desert air may be so dry as to make it virtually impossible for any living thing to exist in it. But, from time to time, it may accumulate enough moisture to deposit dew or to permit rain. And where no living thing was apparent before, desert flowers may spring to life, vast acreages of them coming into full bloom to display a magnificent array of colors. The life of these desert plants may be short, but not so short that they cannot produce seed. And these seed may lie dormant until rain comes again, no matter how long a period that may be. Then they may spring to life and the process will be repeated.

The air of humid regions regularly accumulates so much moisture, derived by evaporation from the open lakes, seas, and the moist soil and by transpiration from lush vegetation, that, on cooling, droplets of water are formed that fall as rain. Later, when the moisture supply in the air has been renewed, rain will come again. Thus the water of Earth is in constant circulation from sea, soil, and plant to air and back again. But the quantity that falls as rain varies greatly from region to region depending on the nature of the movement of the masses of air above. Some of the moisture returns to Earth as dew or fog, some as light showers and some as heavy downpours. And if the temperature of moisture-laden air drops sufficiently, the rain will be transformed into snow, sleet, or hail.

Air may be stiflingly hot under the summer sun. If it is both dry and hot, any moisture that is transpired by plant leaves or respired by man and other animals will disappear as if by magic. If the humidity of the air as well as its temperature is high, conditions may be almost unbearable for living things, particularly for man. In either case, condensation of the moisture in the air by cooling and its return to Earth as rain provide rapid relief.

Air may be so cold as to kill all vegetation and force most of the animal life to seek shelter. At its coldest, virtually all life disappears. Extremes in temperature on the mainland of the United States have been recorded at 130°F. in Death Valley, California, and minus 60°F. in northern Montana. For Earth as a whole the extremes reported have been 136°F. in Azizia, Libya, North Africa, on September 13, 1922, and minus 100.4°F. near the South Pole in Antartica, May 11, 1957.

Air may be clear and pure, it may be hazy, it may be filled with fog, or it may be thick with smog, which is a mixture of fog, smoke, and dust. With adequate movement, air usually clears up under bright sunshine. But on days of virtually complete calm, air in densely populated areas may accumulate smog to the point where plants, animals, and man are in great distress. In October, 1958, dense smog settled over Donora, Pennsylvania, resulting in the deaths of some twenty people. A similar happening occurred some years earlier in the Meuse Valley, Belgium. And in 1952 over four thousand excess deaths resulted from a dense black smog that settled over the city of London.

Great difficulty is experienced in clearing up the air about certain cities, notably Los Angeles, California. There, on calm days, undesirable gases, such as are given off by oil refineries, industrial plants, and automobiles, have accumulated to as much as six times their normal concentrations. Once these gases have collected in any locality there is no means by which they can be dissipated artificially, the only recourse being to wait until a fresh breeze carries them away. But there is the possibility of using preventive measures to do away with their excessive production. A great deal of effort is going into research designed to find means of reducing air pollution.

Dust storms are a troublesome problem in some regions, notably in the western part of the United States. During the dry year of 1954 a dense cloud of dust developed over a large part of Colorado, Kansas, New Mexico, Oklahoma, and Texas. It was fifteen hundred miles long and one thousand miles wide, and it darkened the sky as it moved eastward. Its load of dust was dropped on the land as it advanced, some of it falling on New York and Boston and far out over the Atlantic Ocean.

Disturbances in the air, changes in the temperature, and the fall of rain are manifestations of phenomena operating far out in space away from Earth. They come to pass by way of the relatively shallow envelope of atmosphere that surrounds Earth, extending upward to a height of two hundred miles or more. But nearly 90 per cent of this mass of air, which weighs 14.7 pounds per square inch at sea level, is within twenty miles of Earth's surface.

The gaseous atmosphere above Earth corresponds to the solid lithosphere, or the rock crust of Earth, and the liquid hydrosphere, or the water of the oceans, lakes, and rivers. Of the atmospheric gases, nitrogen constitutes 75.5 per cent by weight; oxygen, 23.02 per cent; argon, 1.43 per cent; and carbon dioxide, 0.046 per cent. If calculated on the basis of volume, the percentages are 78.12, 20.94, 0.93, and 0.03 respectively. The remaining small percentage is made up mostly of neon, helium, methane, nitrous oxide, hydrogen, ozone, and xenon, in descending order by volume.

The atmosphere is always a carrier of moisture. This may not be apparent unless conditions are such that clouds are formed. If these clouds develop near Earth's surface, they are known as fogs. But the atmosphere also carries a great variety of suspended solids, such as soil, ashes, common salt, and particles of soot and other forms of organic matter. Pollen, yeasts, fungi, bacteria, and other minute forms of plant and animal life are also found in the atmosphere. Insects are abundant in the air near the soil, particularly during the summer months in the temperate and arctic regions, but year round in the tropics.

In certain locations, notably near active volcanoes and

around smelters and certain types of industrial plants, the atmosphere often contains considerable amounts of acrid sulfur dioxide. A great variety of other gases are released in other manufacturing processes, such as the colorless and odorless carbon dioxide that is evolved in the combustion of wood and coal and in the production of lime from limestone, the colorless and odorless hydrogen that is given off by oil refineries, and the colorless but pungent ammonia that is evolved from coking plants and that escapes from manure and from compost piles. Of the various other gases that are found occasionally in considerable quantities in the atmosphere, the highly toxic fluorine that is evolved in several industrial processes, notably in the roasting of cryolite in the production of aluminum and in the acidification of phosphate rock in the manufacture of superphosphate, is one of the most troublesome. But the total volumes of this and all other industrial gases is small indeed in comparison to that of the atmosphere as a whole.

The atmospheres of Sun and of the several other planets in the solar system differ materially from each other and from the atmosphere of Earth. The Sun's atmosphere is made up mostly of the gases hydrogen and helium, with only a small proportion of other gases. Mercury has virtually no atmosphere because of her relatively small size and her nearness to Sun. The atmosphere of Venus consists mostly of carbon dioxide, its concentration of this gas being five hundred times that of the atmosphere of Earth. Water vapor is present on Venus, but there is no oxygen. It appears doubtful whether any form of life could exist under such conditions.

Mars, a planet about one-fourth the size of Earth and about 50 per cent farther away from Sun, has an atmosphere containing about ten times as much carbon dioxide as that of Earth. Its atmosphere also contains oxygen and water vapor in sufficient amounts to support simple forms of plant life of the kind known on Earth. In general, however, Mars is an arid planet, no lakes, rivers, or oceans having been observed on it. The pull of gravity of Mars is only about one-third that of Earth, and the weight of its atmosphere per unit area is believed to be only one-fifth that of the atmosphere of Earth.

The atmospheres of Jupiter, Saturn, Uranus, and Neptune appear to be made up largely of hydrogen and helium, with small amounts of methane and ammonia. The clouds noted on Jupiter are believed to consist of crystals of ammonia in a frozen state, the temperature of the atmosphere of that planet being about minus 120°C.

Over 95 per cent of the dry substance of the vegetation on Earth is derived from the atmosphere and hydrosphere. For every 10,000 pounds dry matter of plant material, the annual produce of one acre of good land in the temperate regions, about 4,450 pounds is oxygen, 4,350 pounds is carbon, 625 pounds is hydrogen, and 150 pounds is nitrogen, all originating in air and water. The remaining 425 pounds is mineral matter from the soil.

If vegetative material is completely burned, all of the organic matter is transformed into colorless, odorless gases that are released to the atmosphere—the nitrogen as such, the carbon as carbon dioxide, and the hydrogen and remaining oxygen as water vapor. Only the ash of the plant material, the soil-derived part, remains. Plants are the only agents in nature that can assemble inorganic elements and compounds from air, water, and soil and transform them into organic products, such as the sugars, starches, oils, and proteins. They do this by the aid of Sun. Animals and man do not have this capacity, having to depend on plants to do it for them.

Most of the nitrogen on Earth exists in gaseous form in the atmosphere. The total weight of this atmospheric nitrogen over each acre of land has been estimated at seventy million pounds. A small part of Earth's original supply of nitrogen gas has been joined to oxygen by way of lightning discharges and brought down to the surface of Earth, dissolved in the rainfall of the centuries, where it has been used by plants for the construction of proteins. The total quantity of nitrogen so captured, used, and stored in the soil in the form of plant and animal refuse—the soil organic matter—is approximately three thousand pounds per plowed acre, with possibly an additional three thousand pounds in the total depth of subsoil lying immediately beneath.

The nitrogen that is stored in this soil organic matter, plus the much smaller quantity contained in the living bodies of plants, animals, and man, is only temporarily bound to Earth. In one manner or another it will be gradually released back into the atmosphere from which it came. There, this nitrogen gas circulates freely around the tissues of plants and through the lungs of animals and man without being of any direct use whatever. It has a certain indirect value in that it dilutes the supply of oxygen. Otherwise the rate of respiration of living things and the rate of rotting of soil organic matter might be unduly rapid.

One of the most important and difficult-to-solve problems of agriculture is that of getting sufficient amounts of this relatively inert nitrogen gas of the atmosphere into some combined form, as with oxygen or hydrogen, that will dissolve in water. To some extent this is accomplished by lightning discharges through the atmosphere, which tend to join nitrogen with oxygen in the form that can be brought down to Earth dissolved in the rain. Rain also carries some ammonia, a combination of nitrogen and hydrogen. But this ammonia may be mostly that which escaped from the land during the rotting of organic matter located on top the soil rather than inside it, and during the burning of fuel and the coking of coal. The total amount of these two nitrogen compounds being brought down to Earth dissolved in the rain in humid regions is estimated at from three to five pounds per acre annually. Around industrial areas and in regions of high rainfall it may be considerably more than this; in desert regions it may be much less.

But Nature has much more effective means of capturing gaseous nitrogen from the atmosphere and combining it with other elements to form usable compounds. This is by way of nitrogen-fixing microbes of which the rhizobia that live in the nodules on the roots of legumes are the best example. In addition the azotobacter, which live in the soil independently of legumes and use organic matter as a source of energy in nitrogen fixation, and the blue-green algae, which also have the capacity to fix atmospheric nitrogen, add to the supply that is available for use by crop plants. Yet all of these agencies may not be able to obtain enough fixed nitrogen to meet the need for high acre yields of nonlegume crops.

It was for this reason that so much interest was aroused by Sir William Crookes in 1898, when in an address before the British Association for the Advancement of Science he announced the discovery of a factory method of joining atmospheric nitrogen and oxygen to produce nitrate for fertilizer purposes. Subsequently, it was found that gaseous nitrogen could be made to combine with the hydrogen in natural gas to form ammonia at a much lower cost per unit of fixed nitrogen. Later, still less expensive hydrogen became available for such use from petroleum refineries. Now, factories producing such nitrogen compounds by what is known as a fixation process are widely distributed over the world, every country of any considerable size and technological competence having at least one such nitrogen-fixing factory.

The oxygen of the atmosphere is a much more active gas

than nitrogen. It is this gas that makes it possible to obtain energy from wood, coal, oil, and natural gas in the burning process and resulting fire. Similarly, a slow-burning process without fire takes place in animals and man in which oxygen, taken in through the lungs, is required to produce energy. Even plants, the producers of feeds and foods, consume a part of their own produce within themselves by the aid of oxygen.

The result of all this burning of organic substances—whether fast, as with fire, or slow, as in the microbe, plant, animal, or man—is the production of large volumes of carbon dioxide that is given back to the atmosphere from which it came. This carbon dioxide gas continues to circulate by way of plants, animals, and the organic matter in the soil, back and forth between the atmosphere and Earth. During its temporary stay in living things or in their remains, its carbon and oxygen constitute essential parts of the sugars, starches, oils, and proteins. The animals consuming these plant products temporarily retain part of the carbon and oxygen in the fats and proteins of their bodies. And the microbes that complete the digestion of plant and animal wastes in the soil do likewise.

The carbon dioxide content of the atmosphere is extremely small in comparison to that of nitrogen, being only about 0.03 per cent by volume. Calculated to carbon, the central element in the structure of plants and animals, the atmosphere contains less than one part in 10,000 parts, compared to 7,800 parts of nitrogen per 10,000. Yet the carbon requirement of plants is thirty times that of nitrogen.

The question arises whether this relatively small supply of carbon in the carbon dioxide of the atmosphere is adequate to meet the needs of the highest possible acre yields of plants. Yet Earth's atmosphere contains about 600,000 tons of carbon in the form of carbon dioxide, which is over 1,500 times the estimated annual need of all the vegetation now on Earth.

From time to time evidence has been developed that indicates the possible value of an extra supply of carbon dioxide for plants. Release of extra carbon dioxide from high-pressure cylinders of this gas into greenhouses has resulted in materially increasing the rate of growth and total yield of plants. The likelihood of such good effects is greater in plants grown in culture solutions and in sand or gravel culture than in those grown in organic-matter-rich soils from which carbon dioxide is being continuously released by microbial action. Soils that are high in organic matter are usually very productive, and the extra carbon dioxide escaping from them into the air surrounding the plants may well be one important reason for this. The air in low-lying areas has a higher content of carbon dioxide, a relatively heavy gas, than those at higher elevations. The Mississippi farm boy who produced more than three hundred bushels of corn on one acre, a world record, did it on well-manured soil located in a low-lying valley area.

The carbon dioxide content of the atmosphere is much smaller now than it was earlier in the history of Earth. Tremendous quantities of carbon have been locked up in the vast deposits of coal, petroleum, and natural gas and in those of limestone and coral, having been removed from the atmosphere and stored in the lithosphere. But increasing amounts of this stored carbon are now being returned to the atmosphere in the form of carbon dioxide as these products are consumed by man. An estimated 1,700 billion tons of new carbon dioxide will be returned to the atmosphere during the next fifty years. At expected increased rates of release of carbon dioxide, the temperature of Earth's atmosphere may be raised by as much as two degrees during the next century. This may result in materially increasing the annual acre yields of crop and forest plants.

The lush vegetation that grew during the Carboniferous

period and fell into the swamps to eventually develop into large deposits of peat and, later, coal that now exist in various parts of Earth may have been related to the much higher content of carbon dioxide in the atmosphere at that time. That was some 200 million years ago. It has been suggested that the much colder climate following that period, which resulted in the piling up of huge ice deposits in the Arctic regions and the movement southward of the glaciers of the Ice Age, may also have been related to the reduced amount of carbon dioxide in the atmosphere at that time.

In traveling across the country, whether at home or abroad, most people are quite concerned with what they feel and experience in the way of climate. They are concerned with the nature and appearance of the clouds, the velocity and direction of the winds, and the quantity and intensity of the rainfall. And their attention is automatically drawn to the temperature.

The climates of the various regions of Earth are reflected in the activities and attitudes of people. They are still more evident in the nature and luxuriance of the vegetation. And they are indicated in the color, chemical composition, and physical properties of the soil. When all the climatic factors are joined into one common denominator, the lines drawn between the major climatic regions usually coincide quite closely with those drawn between the correspondingly developed classes of natural vegetation and with those drawn between the major groups of soils. Somewhat similarly developed lines can be drawn between the several ethnic groups of people.

The people of the United States are subject to a changeable climate. The great air masses tend to move from west to east, with relatively rapid successions of high and low barometric pressures. As they move eastward they are alternately affected by cooler winds from the north and warmer winds from the south. These result in marked rises and falls in temperature, with related effects on rainfall.

Temperature drops are often quite sudden, sometimes as much as 20°F. or more within twenty-four hours. The northers that occasionally sweep down from Canada across the Great Plains have been known to lower the temperatures from 90°F. to freezing between noon and midnight. Sometimes they extend their course clear across Texas, as in the case of the cold wave that continued down to the Río Grande Valley in 1951 with temperatures so low that some ten million of the valley's twelve million citrus trees were killed.

Similar cold waves frequently flow far down into Florida, causing serious damage to citrus and vegetable crops. Blustering and sometimes destructive hurricanes, originating in the West Indies, move northward through the Gulf States, on into New England, and out across the eastern tip of Canada. Rain and snow often fall with high intensity, in contrast to what normally occurs in similar latitudes of Europe.

In the spring of 1889 nearly ten inches of rain fell in thirty-one hours at Jamestown, Pennsylvania, with the result that a dam that crossed the river above the city was washed away and 2,000 people were drowned. In 1913, floods along the Ohio River and its tributaries took the lives of some 700 people and destroyed many million dollars worth of property. In 1927 flood waters overflowed some twenty thousand square miles of land along the lower part of the Mississippi River, some 700,000 people being left homeless. In 1955, a week of rains in Oregon and northern California caused seventy-four deaths and property losses of 150 million dollars.

On September 16, 1900, over 6,000 people lost their lives in a hurricane at Galveston, Texas that was moving across the country at a rate of 120 miles an hour. In September, 1928, some 1,800 people were killed when hurricane winds of 160 miles an hour sucked the water out of Lake Okeechobee, Florida, inundating the surrounding area. In September, 1938, high winds moved rapidly across Long Island and eastern New England with resulting loss of some 600 lives and property damage estimated at 330 million dollars. In 1957 hurricane "Audrey," speeding across the country at 97 miles an hour, wiped out Cameron, Louisiana with a loss of 350 lives.

In April, 1937, tornadoes in an area extending from Arkansas to South Carolina resulted in the deaths of 498 people and property losses of 22 million dollars. Over 200 people were killed by tornadoes that spread across Michigan, Ohio, and New England in June, 1953, and property losses amounted to 93 million dollars. In May, 1955, Udall, Kansas and part of Blackwell, Oklahoma were completely destroyed by tornadoes. The record year was 1957, when 924 tornadoes, 230 of them in May, were reported in the United States.

One would think from listening to the radio and reading the newspapers that the people of the United States were being largely destroyed by cyclones and hurricanes, ruined by tornadoes, washed away by floods, frozen by blizzards, melted by extreme summer heat, or choked by dust storms. All these happenings occur from time to time and from place to place. They are of much concern to those directly affected and of great interest to all others. Yet they are relatively uncommon when applied to any one spot or any one person. They are what are known as "climatic accidents."

These ups and downs in weather are believed to be largely responsible for the restless energy of the people of this country. A uniform climate, whether wet or dry or hot or cold, is not nearly so stimulating as a changeable one. And between such drastic changes there are sufficiently long periods of cool and breezy weather in both the northern and southern parts of the mainland of the United States to make ours a stimulating climate. Standing up against the extremes of the elements is an exciting part of life's adventures in this country.

Except for Alaska, the United States has nothing comparable to the continuously low temperatures of Siberia. Its great drouths do not approach the frequency of those in the Ukraine. The hot and rainy monsoons that dominate life in India and Southeast Asia between June and October are unknown in this country. The great typhoons that sweep across Okinawa and the Philippines have no counterpart in our experience. Nothing in the climate of this country is as troublesome as the hot, dry winds that more or less constantly prevail over a vast area in North Africa and across the Near East. And when a period of disagreeably cold, wet weather such as is common in the British Isles and Central Europe comes to pass, it is soon forgotten in the bright sunshine that follows.

Much of the United States is climatically rich. It has heavy rains, interspersed with an abundance of sunshine. It has a temperate climate. Intermittent rainfall and sunshine in a temperate climate permit the growing of a great variety of agricultural plants, virtually every kind that can be grown any place on Earth except for the distinctly tropical types. And all the crop plants can be grown to high levels of production per acre.

The climate of any localized area can often be materially altered by man. The most successful large-scale examples are the many millions of acres of irrigated land in the arid regions of Earth. Large quantities of water are made available for use on arid lands from rivers originating in higher elevations of heavy rainfall, long distances from the areas where irrigation is being practiced. And irrigation practices are being rapidly extended for overcoming seasonal drouths in humid regions, large quantities of water being impounded during periods of heavy rainfall for use later in the year.

Forests serve a highly useful purpose in ameliorating the climate of nearby areas. They act as wind barriers, as agents for increasing infiltration into the soil of the rain and snow that fall, and as aids in preventing loss of the soil itself with consequent devastating effects on the capacity of the land to absorb and retain water. Large areas of land around the Mediterranean Sea and in the Near East that are known once to have been covered with forests are now virtually desert. The famous cedars of Lebanon of Solomon's day are now reduced to a mere five-acre, fence-protected grove surrounded by mountainous desert land that has been overrun by goats, which are believed largely to have been the ultimate cause of the destruction of these forests. Possibly, however, a long-time change in climate was also involved.

To expand agriculture into the frigid zone calls for breeding plants and animals for greater cold-hardiness. Plants must be bred to reach maturity in a shorter period of time. Some help can be realized in limited acreages by covering the soil with powdered coal or by using black paper. Much interest has been aroused in microclimate, which is that near the surface of the soil as distinct from that recorded by the usual meteorological stations that are often located on the tops of tall buildings, or at least, at the height of men's heads.

Parts of the high-rainfall tropics offer great possibilities for agricultural expansion, providing conditions can be made more favorable for man. Once the rain forest has been cleared away and water has been brought under paddy control for the production of rice, a region such as the vast valley of the Amazon River would be capable of producing large tonnages of this highly important food crop. The remaining tropical forests themselves could, no doubt, be put to much more effective use in the more rapid production of tropical timber and in the growing of nuts and fruits if some means of water control could be effected.

Probably the greatest need in the development of humid tropical regions is air conditioning for man. If this were made possible during his sleeping hours, it might well overcome much of the lethargy that tends to overtake the people of the tropics. Refrigeration for food and drink would also have to be developed on a large scale. But neither of these developments is beyond the possibilities for the Amazon River Valley or for similar tropical regions in other parts of the world.

The climate of any region is not a constant. It tends to operate in cycles. Some of these cycles are evident in the concentric rings that are seen in cross-sections of trees. The United States has experienced three serious drouths of record. They occurred around 1860, in 1893–95 and in 1935–38. During the 1935–38 drouth, about 90 per cent of the settlers on the Great Plains abandoned their farms. Wheat production in the area from the Dakotas southward through Texas was cut in half, and corn production was only about one-third that of the predrouth average.

Much longer climatic cycles than these are known to have occurred. The Dark Ages, between the fall of the Roman Empire and the Renaissance, was a warm period in Europe. Cereals were grown in Iceland, wine was produced in Great Britain, settlements were established in Greenland, and the northeastern coast of North America was explored by Norsemen. This heat wave is believed to have reached its peak about A.D. 850. Afterward, the temperature dropped gradually to reach its lowest level about one thousand years later.

Since 1850 the temperature of the Northern Hemisphere has been gradually rising. It is now well on its way to a new peak, which might well occur in or about the year 2850. In the event this happens, vast quantities of ice in the Arctic regions will be changed to water. An over-all rise of 2°F. in the temperature of Earth would, it is believed, melt all the polar ice. In any such event nations like Canada, the Scandinavian countries, and the Soviet Union would be greatly favored in both their agricultural and industrial developments.

But such cycles repeat themselves. Once all the Arctic ice had melted and free circulation of water had set in between the oceans and the polar seas, more rain and snow would fall, glaciers would begin to form and grow, and the next southward invasion of the ice would probably occur. After several thousand years, a deep layer of ice might again cover large parts of North America and northern Europe.

Nothing that is can pause or stay
The moon will wax the moon will wane
The mist and cloud will turn to rain
The rain to mist and cloud again,
Tomorrow be today.

—KERAMOS

Chapter Seven

THE RAIN THAT FALLS UPON US

WATER, the colorless, odorless liquid that is so essential to the well-being of every living thing on Earth, comes nearer to being a universal solvent than any other liquid known. Almost everything water touches will dissolve in it to some degree, and many substances disappear entirely from sight when brought into direct contact with water.

Consequently, water never exists in a pure state in nature. It normally contains at least traces of all the mineral elements found in rocks and soils. Small amounts of most of the gases of the atmosphere, oxygen and carbon dioxide in particular, are found dissolved in the water that falls as rain. And rain also carries ammonia and other gaseous compounds of nitrogen down to Earth. In industrial areas considerable amounts of sulfur dioxide are brought to Earth in rain. There is much truth in the old statement that "rain is fertilizer." This would be true even if the rain were pure water. But the nitrogen- and sulfur-containing gases that are dissolved in it have additional value in that they supply two of the essential nutrient elements required by microbes and higher plants, as well as by animals and man. And the dissolved oxygen in rain water has a highly stimulatory effect on the microorganisms that effect the decay of soil organic matter.

Some substances, such as the original igneous rocks, appear to stand up against the dissolving action of rain. But the many millions of tons of the several salts that are now contained in sea water and the much greater quantities of these salts that are found in large deposits in various parts of Earth provide abundant evidence that a large part of the substance that was contained in these original rocks has been dissolved out of them by the rains of the ages as they disintegrated to form soil. The slowness of this dissolving process was offset by the factor of time.

The sea is the primary source of the water in rain. As this sea water evaporates it leaves behind the substances that were dissolved in it. The principle is the same as that of the heavy lime deposits that build up on the bottom of the teakettle in limestone areas where water is obtained from wells. As the sea became increasingly salty it finally reached saturation, at which point some of the salts separated out and fell to the bottom. The deposits of calcium and magnesium carbonates, from which limestone was made on a tremendous scale, were thus laid down.

Some 80,000 cubic miles of water is evaporated into the atmosphere above the sea every year. Another 15,000 cubic miles of water is added to this supply in the atmosphere by evaporation from the surfaces of inland lakes and from the land, including that transpired by the leaves of plants and that respired by animals and man.

All this water is annually returned to land and sea as rain. Since the sea covers nearly three times as much surface area as the land, it receives the larger part of this return. Thus, of the total quantity of water evaporated annually, an estimated 71,000 cubic miles of it falls back into the sea, leaving 24,000 cubic miles to rain on the land. If all the rain that falls on all the land of Earth fell on the mainland of the United States, it would be equivalent to a layer of water forty feet deep.

Rainfall is not distributed evenly over the surface of Earth. One-third of the land surface of Earth, including a large part of the tundras in the Arctic regions, receives less than ten inches of rain a year. But the rainfall in a number of widely scattered areas, notably in the mountains and the tropics, exceeds 80 inches annually. Some nine million acres of land in the United States has a rainfall of 80 to 100 inches annually and three million acres receive more than 100 inches. On limited areas of Earth the rainfall amounts to as much as 200 inches a year. Over a seventy-four-year period the rainfall at Cherrapunji, India, averaged 450 inches a year. The record is believed to be 471 inches, the average yearly rainfall on Mount Waialeale, Island of Kauai, Hawaiian Islands, for the years 1912–49.

Some of the precipitation is snow, sleet, hail, fog, or dew, but all of it is calculated to its equivalent in rain. An occasional snowfall, like that of the rain, may be very heavy. On December 26, 1947, over 25 inches of snow was deposited in New York City and the surrounding area in twenty hours, almost five inches more than fell during the famous blizzard of March 11–12, 1888, that paralyzed the whole region from Philadelphia to New York and Boston. At Silver Lake, Colorado, seventy-six inches of snow fell in twenty-four hours during the storm of April 14–15, 1921. The average annual snowfall in Rainier Park, Washington, is 575 inches, and during one season it totaled over 1,000 inches. Hailstones, which fall from time to time and place to place, often with great destruction to crops, vary in size from pellets the size of a pea or smaller to those as large as baseballs. And there have been occasional reports of much larger blocks of ice falling from the skies.

Water grows lighter per unit volume as it freezes. This is fortunate, since otherwise ice would sink to the bottom of any body of water on which it was formed. If this occurred, many lakes would contain deposits of ice the year round.

Water flows freely from place to place, seeking an ever lower level. If it soaks into the soil it gradually finds its way downward to some more or less permanent water table, assuming there is a sufficient supply of water to saturate the soil. From such an underground location it may seep out to become a flowing spring, occasionally hundreds of miles from where the rain fell. If the water runs off the surface of the land it will be carried downstream and most of it may ultimately reach the sea.

Dry soil resists wetting. But once it is wet, water usually flows readily across its surface, provided there is an outlet at a lower elevation for its escape. Water is its own lubricating agent. And this same lubricating value is realized in the movement of water into the roots of plants, through the several plant tissues, and out through the stomata on the under sides of the leaves. These stomata are small openings the sizes of which are regulated by guard cells in relation to the supply of water at the plants disposal and the moisture in surrounding air.

Water also serves as a lubricating agent for the passage of the necessary soil-derived nutrients that move from the soil into the plant during its periods of growth, flowering, and fruiting. These dissolved substances usually flow with the stream of water. But they may move at a slower or a faster rate than the water. Under certain conditions substances dissolved in the water in the tissues of plants may move in the reverse direction to that of the flow of water, even escaping back into the soil from which they may have come. Some of the substances that are excreted by plant roots may be organic compounds that were produced inside the plant from the raw materials derived from air, water, and soil.

Water and the soil-derived nutrients move from the soil into the plant. Usually, only the water, and only a part of that, escapes by way of the stomatal openings. On its way through the plant some of the water is withdrawn from the main stream and used as one of the building blocks in the construction of sugars, starches, oils, proteins, and the other organic constituents of plants. But only the hydrogen of the water is used, its oxygen being given off into the atmosphere. Thus a plant serves to purify the air, taking carbon dioxide out of the air, using it in conjunction with the hydrogen of water to make carbohydrate, the first substance produced, and yielding up oxygen to the atmosphere.

From three to five hundred pounds of water are transpired from plants—breathed out through the stomatal openings—for each pound of dry matter produced. A large percentage of the total green weight of a plant is uncombined water that quickly disappears on harvesting and drying the plant in the open air. And still more water can be driven off in a drying oven. Bluegrass, alfalfa, clover, and other forage crops lose water to the extent of 70 to 75 per cent of their green weight on being dried in an oven at 105°C., or a little above the boiling point. Apples, potatoes, tomatoes, and cabbages are from 80 to 90 per cent water. The water content of such grains as corn, wheat, and rice, as they move through trade channels, is about 10 to 15 per cent of their weight.

An acre of good land in the temperate regions of Earth will yield about ten thousand pounds dry matter per crop season. That is about the amount of dry matter in the stalks and grain of a corn crop yielding one hundred bushels an acre. If the loss of water by transpiration was three hundred pounds per pound of dry matter produced, such a crop of corn would have absorbed from the soil and made use of a layer of water more than ten inches deep over the acre during its period of growth.

A mature apple tree may transpire as much as forty gallons of water a day during the active growing season. Calculated on the basis of thirty-two trees an acre, this would indicate a daily need of about five tons of water an acre, plus the amount lost directly from the surface of the soil by evaporation and that used by the tree for new growth and leaf and fruit production. Similarly, vegetables and hay crops transpire large quantities of water and grow best under conditions of a liberal supply of this essential nutrient at all times.

Ordinarily, all this water comes from the rain by way of the soil. In the absence of irrigation, the rate of growth of plants in a field or forest depends largely on the amount of rainfall that can be stored in the soil in a form available to their roots. Once water soaks into the soil, it is held more or less tenaciously by the soil, up to a point approaching saturation. Of this water that is stored in the soil, only a part is available to the roots of the plant growing in the soil. In other words, the soil and plant compete with each other for any water that remains in the soil after any excess of the soil's storage capacity has drained away through underground channels. And dry air flowing over the surface of the land is another competitor of plant and soil for water.

The capacity of soils to retain water against the pull of gravity and that of roots of plants varies greatly, being highest in those containing large amounts of clay and organic matter and lowest in those that are mostly sand. If no additional water is added to the soil by rain or irrigation, the plant will continue to withdraw water from it until the rate of root intake is slowed down to the point where it is less than that at which water is being transpired from the leaves. At this point the plant wilts and growth essentially ceases. But the soil may still contain water equivalent to 10 per cent or more of its dry weight.

Soil storage of water is highly important as a means of tiding a plant over between rains. The amount of such storage depends on the nature of the soil. But the quantity of water at the plant's disposal also depends on the depth to which conditions are favorable for the penetration of its roots, since they tend to grow farther down into the soil as the supplies of available water in the upper layers are exhausted. The roots are seeking the water rather than the water seeking the roots. The roots of most plants grow downward from four to six feet or more in a well-drained soil.

The roots of some plants grow much deeper than this, assuming there is nothing in the subsoil to interfere. In Kansas and neighboring states, where rainfall is relatively limited and the rate of evaporation of water from the land surface is rapid, subsoils are seldom saturated with water for any considerable period of time, if at all. Thus there is nothing to prevent the continued, year-after-year, downward extension of the roots of a perennial plant like alfalfa, which may extend the period of its growth for twenty years or more. Under such conditions the roots of alfalfa plants have been known to grow downward twenty-five feet or more, robbing the soil of its stored moisture as they went. And the roots of perennial grasses may do likewise. This may have serious consequences since, if for any reason the land is plowed in preparation for planting a new crop, only the deep-down supplies of stored water remain, and the crop may not survive a drouth long enough for its roots to reach to water depth.

The portion of the total precipitation, including the rain, snow, dew, and fog that will be available for crop production during any given period depends on how much of it is stored in the soil in available form, how much of this is lost from the surface of the soil by evaporation, and how much of it is required to be transpired from the leaves of the plants. A value known as the precipitation-evapotranspiration ratio has been found useful in arriving at the boundaries of the several climatic zones of Earth.

This ratio must be thought of in terms of the land in its virgin state where loss of water by way of underground drainage and surface runoff is determined by nature rather than as modified by man. Maps developed from precipitation data alone differ markedly from those obtained by the use of precipitation-evapotranspiration-ratio data. The latter maps have a strong reselmblance to those showing the natural vegetation areas of the region under study.

In the United States, for example, lines connecting points of equal precipitation tend, by and large, to run north and south, particularly through the corn and wheat areas of the central states. Thus the line connecting points having an average annual precipitation of twenty inches extends southward from the Dakotas through Nebraska, Kansas, Oklahoma, and Texas. Lines connecting points of equal potential evapotranspiration values tend to run east and west. Thus the twenty-seven-inch line of yearly potential evapotranspiration starts in New Jersey and extends across Pennsylvania, Ohio, and Indiana and through Illinois and Iowa to Nebraska.

The effective moisture supply, represented by the ratios of

these two sets of values, is best shown by the natural vegetation that existed over what is now the United States of America when the first European settlers arrived. Beginning at the east coast the land was covered with dense forests of deciduous trees. These merged into a mixed growth of deciduous and evergreen forests to the northeast and mostly pine forests to the southeast. West of this tree belt was a vast area of land that was covered mostly with tall grasses, constituting the prairies. Farther west the Great Plains were covered with short grasses. And still farther west the typical vegetation of semiarid and arid lands appeared. In the Pacific Northwest, where rainfall was also heavy, dense forest vegetation again appeared.

Since water is so essential for the growth of crop plants, ever greater effort is being made to store more of that which falls as rain and snow. These measures have value not only in terms of saving water for later use but for preventing loss of soil by water erosion. The problem is one of getting as much as possible of this water to soak into the soil where it falls, any excess being removed by natural underground drainage channels or by those provided by man.

The starting point in getting water to soak into the soil of rolling land is to farm it on the contour. This calls for working the land on the level across the slope rather than up and down the slope. As far as feasible, the land is kept covered with close-planted vegetation, such as small grains, grasses, forests, and cover crops. Where it must be cultivated during the crop season, as usually applies to cotton, corn, vegetables, and similar row crops, modern practice calls for leaving as much as possible of the refuse of previous crops on the surface to break the fall of the raindrops on the soil and permit greater infiltration of the water into the soil.

When the rain at any one time and place is so heavy that some of it will run off the surface whatever special measures have been taken to prevent this, some method of control of the surplus water must be provided. So far as any particular farmer's fields are concerned, the best means of easing this water down the slope to stream-bed levels is by way of fairly wide, shallow channels that are kept permanently covered with grass.

Since streams of water may grow in volume from those of the tiny rivulets of springs at the start of a watercourse to rain-carrying creeks that grow into ever larger rivers, provision must be made for the control of their accumulated waters at times of abnormally heavy rainfall within the individual watersheds. Two agencies in the United States endeavor to merge their efforts in such control of water. One of these is the Soil Conservation Service of the United States Department of Agriculture and the other is the Army Corps of Engineers.

The Soil Conservation Service thinks of this water as something to be saved; therefore, with the aid of the Soil Conservation District supervisors and the farmers of their districts, the Service endeavors to get as much as possible of it to soak into the soil where it falls. The surplus is carried off by way of grass-covered channels and emptied into the nearest streams. But these creeks, of ever growing size downstream, may build up to flood proportions in time of heavy rainfall. Accordingly, efforts are made to provide upstream storage behind dams thrown across the streams so that downstream build-up is delayed. In general, these upstream dams are multiple purpose dams. They are built on the assumption that they will store water for at least two purposes. One of these is for flood prevention and the other is for saving water for later use in irrigating cropland. But there is nothing to prevent the use of this stored water for growing fish or for swimming and other recreational purposes. To effect all these purposes the dams must be built higher than would otherwise be required.

The Army Corps of Engineers deals more largely with the

downstream build-ups of water that lead to disastrous floods over large areas of land toward the mouths of the great rivers. Their purpose is to control the flow of excess water so that it moves as quickly as possible into ever larger streams and on out to sea. This calls for straightening stream courses and building long levees and big dams of the expensive type, in comparison to the relatively small unit costs of the upstream water control and storage measures. These two concepts of management of excess water can be merged at some point along the line of the flow of water to good effect.

In areas of deficient rainfall a primary problem is that of obtaining water from some not-too-distant area of heavy rainfall and conducting it to the points of need. The collecting points for this water are usually mountain ranges where the air currents, on rising to pass over the mountains, cool and drop their loads of water. The waterholding capacity of the air at 70°F. is only one twenty-fifth as much as it is at 100°F., and at 50°F. it is only one-fiftieth.

Vast irrigation projects to carry water from far distant mountainous regions of high rainfall to desert areas were undertaken long before the Christian Era in Assyria, Babylonia, Egypt, China, India, Greece, and Rome. And many millions of acres of land in these and other countries are still under irrigation, with ever greater plans for collecting and storing more water for such purposes.

Some 27 million acres of land in the western half of the United States is now being irrigated, and enough more water is available for possibly 20 million acres more. But rapid growth in population along the West Coast requires that more and more of this water be reserved for city and industrial use. This increasing demand for water has made it necessary to give serious consideration to means by which the supplies of water can be increased. Of these, the possibilities of making it rain more frequently and in larger amounts and of taking the salt out of sea water are the most important.

A great deal of exploratory work has been done toward developing means of making it rain, particularly in connection with supplying more water to the semiarid and arid regions of the United States. Many clouds that are capable of supplying water move across the country without dropping their loads on the land. Much of the water in these clouds is dumped into the ocean. The problem is one of locating such clouds while they are over the land and treating them in such a manner to cause the water to condense and come down as rain or snow.

Two methods of cloud seeding have been widely employed. One is an over-seeding procedure in which dry ice—solid carbon dioxide—is dropped into the clouds by airplane from above. The other involves the use of silver iodide smoke that is driven up from beneath the clouds by ground-based blowers. The average increase in rainfall from seeding clouds is estimated to be between 5 and 22 per cent, with one chance in ten that it will be above or below these percentages.

Cloud-seeding operations have given the most dependable results on the windward slopes of the mountains along the Pacific Coast, and especially during the late winter and early spring months. This permits the belief that much more water might be available for irrigation purposes in arid areas that are located within reach of these mountains by canal.

Further study of this problem should result in the development of techniques by which more rain could be made to fall not only in these mountains but in other areas as well. The latest development along this line is that suggested by scientists of the Naval Weather Service who propose to release carbon black, a finely divided product, inside the clouds. These black particles of carbon absorb the heat of the Sun, lose some of their moisture by evaporation, and thus tend to build up the moisture content of the air in between. Once enough water is collected at any point to form a droplet, this droplet tends to set off the rain-making process as it falls through the cloud.

There is considerable evidence to indicate that it might be possible to make rain fall with greater regularity and at more suitable intervals across the entire United States by regular applications of cloud-seeding materials. Such studies have been conducted over considerable periods of time under the direction of scientists of the General Electric Company, with quite promising results.

Purification of sea water for agricultural use is an intriguing subject. Methods of separating water from salts that are dissolved in it are well-known. These include distillation, electrodialysis, osmosis, and freezing, which involve the use of heat, electric current, exchange resins, and refrigeration techniques, respectively. The problem is one of relative costs. Since no very large-scale plants are in operation as yet, the costs can be calculated only from small pilot plants. Such estimates may not apply to operations of giant size that would certainly be required for these purposes.

The price the consumer can afford to pay for water depends upon the use he expects to make of it. If a man was dying of thirst, the cost of any pure water he might be able to come by would be essentially immaterial. For city users in general an effort is generally made not to allow the cost of water to exceed thirty-five cents per thousand gallons. Industrial users in the United States might be willing to pay as much as three dollars per thousand gallons. But for agricultural use, where the value of water is measured in terms of what the extra produce can be sold for, the cost under present conditions cannot exceed about twelve cents per thousand gallons.

It is conceivable, of course, that it may be found necessary in due time to take large quantities of water from the sea, even though costs of purification are somewhat higher than those mentioned. But it is also possible that greatly improved means of separating sea water from the salts dissolved in it will be developed whereby the costs may be materially lowered. The lowest estimate by methods now known is sixty cents per thousand gallons for large-scale operations.

The costs of purifying water referred to are at the point of origin, which is at the seashore and at sea level. But the need for water for agricultural use is usually far inland from the sea, and at considerably higher elevations than the sea. Movement of purified sea water to such points of need will add greatly to its cost applied to the land. Only a relatively small percentage of the total area of desert and semiarid land in the United States, which totals some 750 million acres, is likely ever to be irrigated with water from the Pacific Ocean.

Even in areas of adequate rainfall, as measured by the average amount of rain that falls per year, there are frequently troublesome periods of drouth. These may result in materially reducing acre yields or in the complete destruction of crops. During the great national drouth of 1932–38, the crops in the states west of the Mississippi River were poor indeed. In the middle of the summer of 1936, one driving across these states saw scarcely a green leaf in the fields or on the trees, except along the watercourses. Occasional fields of deep-rooted alfalfa were able to survive by reaching ever farther down below the surface for water stored at still lower depths.

There are various means of combating the effects of such drouths. Crops of greater drouth resistance can be bred and grown. Larger amounts of the falling rain can be saved by improved methods of soil management that are designed to increase infiltration of water into the soil and storage for summer use. A great deal of attention is being given to supplemental irrigation, which is quite a different matter from that of using irrigation water in arid regions where no crop whatever could be produced without the water thus supplied.

Since the annual rainfall of humid regions, on the average, is more than adequate for the production of high acre yields of the crops normally grown, enough water can often be stored during periods of surplus rainfall to meet the needs for supplemental irrigation in occasional periods of drouth. One such storage system calls for upstream dams that are built primarily as an aid to flood prevention but with the further thought of saving water for irrigation purposes. Another calls for the construction of farm ponds, many thousands of which have been built in the United States during the last quarter century. These ponds not only provide water for supplemental irrigation but for livestock, fishing, and recreational purposes as well. Supplemental irrigation is being applied to some three million acres of cropland in the eastern half of the United States.

In many parts of the extensive coastal plain along the Atlantic Ocean and the Gulf of Mexico, a more or less permanent water table can be reached at a depth of ten to twenty feet below the surface. The soil is so sandy that the rainfall, which is relatively high in that region, percolates downward readily to maintain these supplies of water. And additional water, which often comes to the surface in ever flowing springs and artesian wells, reaches these areas through underground channels from the mountain-covered areas farther inland.

Water rights are a troublesome problem. The principle of riparian rights, which involves the privilege of using water that flows through one's property in accordance with prior established practice, is being reconsidered in relation to the needs of all the people within the several great watersheds. Conflicts of interest occur not only between individual owners of land but between farmers and townsmen, and between towns, cities, counties, and states. Studies have been made in a number of states in preparation for remedial legislation.

It would appear that a farmer will always be entitled to the privilege of conserving and using all the rain that falls on his own land, even if he cannot help himself to all the water that may flow through his property. The building of farm ponds and the adoption of any improved practices that will result in making more of the rain soak into the soil are certainly within his rights, and he is taking ever greater advantage of them.

Whatever precautions may be taken to hold water back by upstream dams and to speed its flow downstream by straightening channels and building levees so that it can hurry on faster to the sea, disastrous floods will continue to occur. These are due to abnormally high intensity of rainfall for considerable periods of time, sometimes locally and sometimes over wide areas in a given watershed. Such excessive rainfall may come only once in fifty years, once a century, or once in a thousand years. But when it comes, our man-made structures may be unable to contain it.

Great losses of life and property such as are believed to have occurred in the land of Canaan in Noah's time around 3000 B.C. and are known to have taken place during the first great flood of record along the Yellow River in 2297 B.C. are still occurring from time to time and place to place over the surface of Earth. And there is every reason to believe that many more such floods will occur in the years ahead.

The increasingly high loss of life and the ever greater damage to property from floods arise from the fact that people tend to settle and develop towns and cities on the flood plains of rivers because of their relatively flat topography and the great depths of rich alluvial soil that cover them. Some 500 million people in India, China, and other nations of southeastern Asia are located on such land, where they grow rice. And an ever increasing number of people in the United States are building their homes and factories in such locations. The disastrous flood that occurred along the Missouri River at Kansas City, Missouri, in July, 1951, was a relatively recent reminder that a great deal more must be done in the United States if further serious losses of life and property on such flood plains are to be avoided.

In some areas floods are repeated with considerable regularity, and heavy expenditures for their control can readily be justified. But many floods occur at unexpected times and in unexpected places. This applies particularly to those following severe thunderstorms, which occur almost anywhere, including the desert. Similar irregularity of time and place of occurrence is shown with storms arising in the tropics that move across the country as typhoons and hurricanes. And snow accumulations in the cooler and moister regions of Earth present great hazards that often materialize into heavy damage from avalanches or from floods with the coming of warm spring rains.

Continued growth in population and industry and improvements in standards of living are resulting in a rapid increase in the consumption of water in cities and suburban areas. And many modern developments, such as the construction and paving of ever larger mileages of streets and highways of ever greater width, tend to greatly increase the amount and rate of runoff of rain without its having served a very useful purpose.

Extensive water-pumping operations for city and farm use have already so lowered the water table in regions of low or essentially no rainfall-renewal of water supplies that costs of pumping are becoming prohibitive. One such location is that near Lubbock, Texas, where a large underground reservoir of water has been tapped for irrigation purposes. This is a region of relatively low and undependable rainfall. And, as yet, no satisfactory solution for the renewal of this water supply has been devised or found.

A similar problem is presented in cities that are located along the seaboard, where water is obtained from wells. As the population grows and water consumption increases, the water table is often lowered to the point where trouble is experienced with seepage of sea water into the ground-water supplies that are being used. This may occur even in regions of relatively high rainfall.

A great deal of attention is being given to the underground storage of water from excess flow in rivers and from occasional heavy downpours in arid areas. And the same principle applies to the re-use of industrial waters by way of storage wells in the humid regions. In some localities the effluent from city sewage-disposal plants and the runoff from city streets is being collected and stored in underlying sandy strata.

More and more attention will have to be given to every phase of the problem of maintaining adequate supplies of fresh water. There is good reason to believe that this problem can be solved in most areas by application of several techniques that are now being experimented with. But a great deal more work along this line will have to be done.

It can be expected, however, that the cost of fresh water in cities, in relation to the cost of other goods and services, will increase materially in comparison to what people have been accustomed. And it may be that pure water will come to have much greater value to everyone, relative to other wants and needs, than it does now. In any event, water that falls as rain is free, except for the cost of accumulating it and delivering it without contamination to the points of need. And rain, therefore, is likely to become even more appreciated as one of the most important and essential gifts of nature.

The whole of life is, in its simplest terms, a struggle for free energy, whether it be between shrub and tree for a place in the Sun, between locust and rabbit for the energy-building compounds of leaves, or between lion and tiger for the flesh of the antelope. Free energy all living things must have, for without it change is petrified—and change is life.

—RALPH W. GERARD

Chapter Eight

OUR PLACE IN THE SUN

THE Colossus of Rhodes, a huge bronze statue of a giant bearing a torch in his uplifted hand with a foot firmly planted on the land on each side of the river that flowed into the principal harbor of the Island of Rhodes in the Mediterranean Sea and with the ships passing between his legs, was built in honor of Helios, the sun god. Twelve years were spent in designing and constructing this famous statue, one of the Seven Wonders of the World. Completed in 280 B.C., unfortunately the statue was destroyed by an earthquake fifty-six years later.

This great work of Chares was an indication of the awe and reverence in which Sun was held by the people of ancient Greece. Helios, sometimes known as Apollo, was credited with driving his flaming chariot across the sky from east to west, starting each morning after the Hours had harnessed and hitched his four horses to it. And each day Helios returned faithfully to perform his dangerous mission. Milton, commenting on this performance, wrote: "Now the guided car of day his golden axle doth allay in the steep Atlantic stream. And the slope Sun his upward beam shoots against the dusky pole, pacing towards the other goal of his chamber to the East." It is little wonder that the then unpredicted eclipses of Sun that darkened Earth during the day from time to time and sent the chickens to roost were viewed with great consternation and alarm. And these fears still persist among many of the less enlightened peoples of Earth.

Man and Earth were long thought to be the center of the universe. It was believed that Sun revolved around Earth. But this concept was finally dispelled with proof that the reverse was true. Sun finally came to be recognized as the center of a solar system of which Earth constituted only a small part, even though that part is highly important to the people who live on it. But it may be well to be reminded that Sun is now known to be a mere dwarf among the many suns (stars) one sees in the skies during a clear night. And beyond the solar system, with which man is reasonably familiar, are many stellar systems, called galaxies, which constitute the universe. The stars are numbered in billions, and millions of planets like Earth are believed to be revolving around them.

But Sun is extremely important to the people who inhabit Earth. Although it is 93 million miles away from Earth, its rays, traveling at the rate of 186,300 miles a second, not only light the way for man but provide the heat that makes existence possible for him on Earth. Its surface temperature is around 11,000°F. The light energy of Sun is transformed by green plants into chemical energy that is released when the resulting feeds and foods are digested by animals and man or by the microbes that inhabit the soil. Or it can be released by fire. And the heat energy of Sun, acting directly on Earth and its atmosphere, raises the temperature to a point that makes Earth a suitable place for living things.

Sun is a mass of hot gases and of elements of which rocks are made. It is rushing through space in the general direction of the bright star Vega at a rate of about twelve miles a second. It is a relatively small part, but to man a highly important part, of the universe, which is believed to be a rapidly expanding system in space. Sun has a diameter of 866,500 miles, more than one hundred times that of Earth. Around it revolve nine planets, celestial bodies born of Sun but which, presumably, have been pulled away from it under the disruptive influence of other passing stars. Mercury, the smallest of these planets, is nearest Sun. Venus, the evening star, is the second planet out from Sun. And Earth is the third planet in the series.

Since man lives on Earth, he knows a great deal more about it than he does about the other planets in the solar system. This knowledge provides a clue for an understanding of Sun and all the planets that revolve around it. Earth undoubtedly consisted of much the same kind of matter as Sun. But it has cooled down during the several billion years of its separate existence and now supports a great variety of forms of life on its surface. Yet Earth still has a very hot interior.

Earth rotates on its axis every twenty-four hours, which gives us our days and nights. It revolves around Sun along a 600-million-mile orbit once each year at a speed of over eighteen and one-half miles a second. Because of the inclination of Earth's axis from the vertical, the four seasons come into play. The diameter of Earth at the Equator is 7,927 miles.

On beyond Earth in the solar system are five other planets. Of these, Jupiter, which is 367 million miles farther from Sun than Earth, is the largest. Pluto, the planet farthest removed from Sun and most recently discovered, is 3,367 million miles away. Sun is extremely large in comparison to all the planets and their satellites, constituting 99.8 per cent of the total mass of the entire solar system. As would be expected, the planets nearest Sun have the highest temperatures and those farthest away the lowest. Thus the temperature on Mercury is hundreds of degrees above zero Fahrenheit, and that on Jupiter is of the order of 200°F. below zero. That on Pluto is still much colder.

The heat energy of Sun, radiated out into space, is the primary source of the energy that controls the temperature of Earth. Present climatic conditions vary directly in relation to solar phenomena. Past changes in climate probably did not differ materially in kind from those of recent years, but they differed greatly in degree. Thus it has been much warmer and much colder on Earth than it is today.

The heat energy from Sun is received directly at the outer surface of Earth's atmosphere at a mean rate of 1.94 calories per square centimeter per minute. This is known as the solar constant. A calorie is the amount of heat required to raise the temperature of one gram of water one degree Centigrade at a pressure of one atmosphere. A centimeter is 0.3937 inch. A gram is 0.0353 ounce. Of every one hundred units of Sun's heat energy that reach Earth's atmosphere, thirty-five are reflected back into space by the atmosphere. The remaining sixty-five units reach the surface of Earth and serve necessary purposes in regulating its temperature, in evaporating water from sea and land, and in making it possible for plants and animals, including man, to grow and reproduce their kind.

The solar constant is not really a constant. It fluctuates within a range of about 2 per cent. Since 1925 a net increase in temperature of about 0.3 per cent has been observed. This means that a gradual warming-up of Earth's atmosphere has been taking place. Temperatures in other periods of Earth's history have risen and fallen over longer, and possibly shorter, periods.

The 2 per cent fluctuation in the solar constant is known to be related to sunspots. These are violent eruptions on the surface of Sun. They cover vast areas of its surface, having diameters varying between 1,000 and 100,000 miles. The annual number of sunspots since 1750, the first year for which records are available, has varied between 46 in 1816 and 155 in 1947. These variations are cyclic, the periods between the minimum and the maximum numbers averaging about eleven years. This means that the corresponding climatic cycles tend to repeat themselves every twenty-two years.

Good correlation has been observed between sunspot numbers and the weather as measured by temperature and precipitation. With low sunspot numbers the weather in the high-middle latitudes has been cold and dry and that in the low-middle latitudes has been cold and wet. Storm tracks have migrated equatorward and glaciers have expanded. With high sunspot numbers the weather in the high-middle latitudes has been warm and dry and that in the low-middle latitudes warm and wet. Storm tracks have migrated polarward and glaciers have shrunk.

A possible relationship has been postulated between high numbers and intensities of sunspots and the prevalence of great plagues, such as cholera or Black Death. Such plagues usually follow famines, attacking people when they are in a highly vulnerable, undernourished state. And famines in turn tend to follow drouths, which are associated with high sunspot activity. Mentally disturbed people are often quite sensitive to high intensity of sunspots. It has been suggested that financial panics occur most frequently during the warmer and less invigorating weather that precedes periods of great sunspot activity. Thus man may be influenced by Sun to a much greater degree than is generally realized if one thinks only in terms of heat and cold and day and night.

The light energy of Sun operates on an entirely different basis from that of its heat energy. It has special value in connection with the growing of green plants and the carbon-fixing processes that take place in them by which this light energy is transformed into chemical energy. And this chemical energy can then be transformed into heat energy, as occurs during the digestion of feeds and foods by animals and man and by the microbes in the soil. This energy release is most apparent, however, when it is accomplished by the use of fire, as in a wood grate or a furnace.

About one-half of Sun's light energy that reaches Earth is visible. The other half consists of rays that are longer or shorter than the visible rays. The longer wave lengths, known as infrared light, have heat effects. The shorter wave lengths, known as ultraviolet light, constitute only a small part of the total, but they have important photographic and chemical effects. For example, they are responsible for the production of vitamin D in food as well as in the skin of man when exposed to sunlight. The disease known as rickets is due to a deficiency of vitamin D. Bone development is abnormal and restricted, the affected animals being small and malformed. Bowleggedness in children is an example of the deformities that occur under conditions of a limited supply of vitamin D. This is a result of inability to fully utilize the calcium and phosphorus that are required in the building of a firm bony structure when this vitamin is lacking.

The visible light of Sun supplies most of the energy required by the chloroplasts of green plants in which an important photosynthetic process takes place. This involves the joining of the carbon dioxide that is absorbed by the leaves from the atmosphere with the hydrogen of water that is absorbed by the roots.

The resulting product is a precursor of sugar. In other words, the first product formed, when joined to other molecules of the same kind, becomes a simple sugar such as glucose. And further polymerization, or joining together of these units, occurs in which complex long-chain molecules of sucrose are formed. In sugar beets and sugar cane, sucrose accumulates. In most other plants it is changed to starch, as in cereal grasses, or to cellulose, as in cotton and other plant fibers. And in still other plants, as in trees, a much more complex compound known as lignin is produced in quantity.

But these first simple compounds may end up as oils, which are more concentrated forms of chemical energy than sugars and starches. Thus the energy released in the burning of one gram of carbohydrate, such as sucrose, is 4,150 calories, in comparison to 9,400 calories from one gram of oil. When nitrogen is added to the molecule it is transformed into an amino acid. And when a series of amino acids are joined to form a polymerized molecule, it becomes a protein. The energy value for one gram of average protein is 5,650 calories.

The rate of uptake of carbon dioxide by green plants and the rate at which sugars, starches, cellulose, oils, and proteins are produced depend not only on the light energy received from Sun but on the heat energy as well. The temperature of the soil and air must be some place between about 40°F. and 100°F. Thus, no matter how much sunlight may be at the plant's disposal, carbon fixation does not take place either in cold weather or in extremely hot weather.

This carbon fixation, and the production of sugars and other substances derived from the original fixation product, is accomplished by the chloroplasts in plant leaves. These chloroplasts are made up of small *grana,* or grains, that contain the chlorophyll, or green-coloring matter, of green plants. One square inch of leaf surface may contain as many as one billion cells, each containing fifty chloroplasts. In each of these chloroplasts there may be one hundred *grana*. And each *grana* may contain ten million molecules of chlorophyll. Under the influence of visible light these chlorophyll molecules carry on their carbon-fixing processes. About 95 per cent of the dry weight of plants consists of the organic products so synthesized. The mineral elements obtained from the soil, and constituting the other 5 per cent, served as catalyzers of this carbon-fixing process. These synthesized products include not only those already mentioned but vitamins, enzymes, alkaloids, organic acids, and a great variety of additional organic compounds that give particular plants their peculiar odors, flavors, and other characteristics, some of which are readily apparent to the consumer and others of which are not.

Nearly half the total dry weight of plants is carbon. The land plants of Earth accumulate carbon in quantities estimated at 19 billion tons, equivalent to 50 billion tons of sugar, annually. The amount of carbon fixed by sea plants is believed to be seven or eight times these quantities. The carbon fixers of the sea are not so much the seaweed as the algae and diatoms, the "grass of the sea." These are microscopic forms of plant life constituting the major part of the plankton inhabiting the sea. The plankton include the minute forms of both plants and animals which are found mostly in the surface waters.

Adding all these quantities, it would appear that the total annual photosynthetic production of carbon compounds by all the various forms of green plant life, both on the land and in the sea, is about the equivalent of 300 billion tons of sugar a year. This is believed to be over one hundred times the weight of all the products of all the mining, metallurgical, and chemical industries on Earth.

A close relationship exists between the length of day to which plants are exposed and their flowering and fruiting. This soon becomes apparent when one attempts to grow plants in latitudes far removed from those to which they have long been accustomed. Some plants do not bloom unless the days are relatively long. Others bloom when the days are relatively short. And still others bloom no matter what the lengths of night and day. Blooming and fruiting are merely indexes of other deep-seated phenomena that are governed by light.

The chrysanthemum is a good example of a plant that will not bloom during the middle of the summer in a temperate climate, delaying this process until the period of daylight has been reduced to thirteen and one-half hours or less in the autumn. All that is necessary to induce earlier blooming is to cover the plants with black cloth during a part of each day, and this is being done on a large scale by commercial growers, notably those in Florida.

The farther north a locality in the northern hemisphere, the longer the long days and the shorter the short days of the year. At the border between the United States and Canada the longest days are two hours longer and the shortest days are two hours shorter than the corresponding days along the Gulf Coast. Furthermore, the dawn and the twilight are much longer in the northern latitudes.

In this light relationship is to be found, at least in part, the explanation of the difference in crop yields depending on the latitudes in which these crops are grown. Herein may lie, in large part, the explanation of the relatively high percentage of sugar in Michigan beets, the relatively high acre yields of Maine potatoes, and the relatively high bushel weights of Scottish oats, in comparison to the lower yields and weights, respectively, of these crops when grown in areas farther south.

But temperatures are also involved. The corn belt comprises the region in which the mean summer temperature is between 70°F. and 80°F., and the night temperature averages approximately 60°F. The period between frosts is more than 140 days. And the precipitation is between twenty-five and fifty inches, seven inches of which should occur during July and August. The major portion of the corn belt in the United States comprises western Ohio, the whole of Indiana, Illinois, Missouri and Iowa, eastern Kansas and Nebraska, southern Wisconsin and Minnesota, and South Dakota. Very little corn is grown in Central Europe, the climate being much more favorable for wheat and oats.

Winter wheat thrives best in those areas where the climate is cool and moist during the fall, winter, and spring months and then gradually develops into a warm, bright, and somewhat dry harvest period. It is apparent that a good winter-wheat climate is not the same as that described for corn. Nevertheless, these crops overlap somewhat, since wheat is essentially a winter- and spring-grown crop, whereas corn is a summer crop.

Oats are also adapted to cool, moist climates but are much more seriously affected by high temperatures than is wheat. Not only are yields much lower in southern latitudes of the Northern Hemisphere but the weight per bushel is considerably less. Yet this can be overcome in southern latitudes by sowing oats in the fall and growing them during the winter months.

Potatoes grow best in cool, moist climates, somewhat north of the corn belt in the United States and in the regions of high acre yield of wheat and oats in northern Europe. Here again, by planting potatoes in the fall they can be grown successfully and to high acre yields in the southern states.

The sugar beet is another crop that grows best and develops its highest sugar content in regions of cool, moist climate. On the other hand, sugar cane grows best and produces the most sugar under conditions in which the temperature is uniformly high, sunlight is bright, and showers are frequent.

Cotton is a highly important warm-climate crop in the United

States. The northern limit for cotton growing is approximately a mean summer temperature of 77°F. and a frostless season of two hundred days. The best cotton is produced when the weather is warm and moderately moist from April to August and when it is dry and cool during the autumn picking period. On the other hand, cotton can withstand periods of drouth and still recover and produce satisfactory yields if the season later becomes more favorable.

Rice has high water requirements, being grown to best advantage under paddy conditions as in southeastern Asia, or under irrigation as in the southern United States. Temperature requirements for rice are at least 75°F. as a mean during the crop season.

Olives and grain sorghums are two examples of drouth-resistant crops. The olive is sensitive to frost but grows well in arid regions, notably in southern Europe and North Africa. Large acreages of grain sorghums are grown in Texas, Oklahoma, and Kansas, where temperature conditions are favorable for corn but moisture conditions are not. During periods of drouth, grain sorghum ceases growing, but it resumes growth when rain comes.

Of the fruits, apples and cherries do best in the cooler climates to the north, peaches and plums somewhat farther south, and grapes and citrus fruits in still warmer climates. Here and there these fruits are grown in other latitudes when conditions have been altered, as by the presence of large inland bodies of water in the Great Lakes region, where grapes are grown.

By breeding and selecting, all of these crop plants can be made to grow outside the normal boundaries in the direction of more heat or cold, longer or shorter days, or more or less rainfall. At the same time they may be made more resistant to the attacks of diseases and insects, which are adapted to the same climatic conditions as the crops on which they prey. By natural selection these pests may later spread into areas that were once unfavorable for them.

A great deal of study is being directed toward unlocking the secrets of the chlorophyll molecule. Just how does chlorophyll effect the separation of the hydrogen of water from its oxygen, the joining of this hydrogen to the carbon dioxide to produce a simple sugar, and the releasing of its oxygen to the atmosphere? Such studies are being carried out by scientists whose primary interest is in finding out the facts without necessary reference to any particular use that may be made of them.

But once the exact mechanism of this process is known, there are those who would be greatly interested in the possibility of putting this information to work on a factory basis, separate and apart from living plants. Some scientists believe it may be possible in due time to develop factory procedures for food production that can replace the present field economy. They visualize putting sugar production on a factory belt-line basis, and then using bacteria and yeasts for transforming this sugar into fats, proteins, vitamins, and other essential food substances in large factories especially designed for these purposes. This would be revolutionary indeed. But it is not beyond the realm of possibility. The economy of such methods of feed and food production in comparison to their production in the field is doubtful, at least for the present.

A considerable amount of study has been applied to the production of algae, notably the genus known as *Chlorella.* These are being grown in an experimental way in large shallow tanks of water containing the necessary mineral nutrients and suitable supplies of soluble nitrogen fertilizers. The resulting product, when dried, has a pleasant odor and a protein content approaching that of beans or peas. Here again, use is being made of the green chlorophyll and its capacity to join the carbon dioxide of the atmosphere with the hydrogen of water.

The carbon-fixing process in photosynthesis has great value over and above that represented by the feeds and foods thus produced. It serves to purify the air for animals and man. The effect is not only to remove excess carbon dioxide from the air but to release oxygen to it. Otherwise, the carbon dioxide given off in the digestion of feeds and foods by animals and man, in the decay of soil organic matter, in the combustion of fuels, and in the burning of limestone would accumulate in toxic concentrations. Green plants, therefore, serve as agents for regulating the composition of the atmosphere within the limits suited not only to themselves but to all the other living things on Earth.

Only a small fraction of the light energy of Sun that falls on the leaves of plants is utilized in photosynthesis. Much of it is reflected back into the atmosphere, transmitted through the leaves, used in transpiration of water during its movement through plants, or radiated as heat.

A considerable amount of work has been done toward making better use of the sunshine that falls on buildings or in waste places, such as the vast deserts of Earth. By proper location of buildings with reference to the angle of incidence of Sun's rays and by use of wide expanses of glass, enough heat can be accumulated in temperate climates to develop adequate supplies of hot water or even to heat homes. Sun's rays are also being concentrated by mirrors for use in cooking in areas deficient in stored fuels.

Tremendous quantities of Sun's energy of past ages have been stored in the coal, petroleum, and natural gas resources of Earth. For the most part the carbon fixed in all these fuels is believed to have had its origin in the atmosphere and to have been accumulated by the agency of the chlorophyll of green plants. The day-by-day release of energy from Sun is not adequate to control the temperature of the atmosphere at livable levels during the winter months of the year. Consequently, supplemental heat is being derived from the combustion of these fossil fuels. From time to time there arises the question of how long it will be until the known reserves of these fuel resources have been exhausted. So far, the rate of discovery of new deposits has been more rapid than the rate of exhaustion of the old deposits.

There are, of course, other possible sources of energy, including those of the winds, the tides, and falling water. All of these can be harnessed for the production of electric energy to replace the energy of natural fuels. Then there are the possibilities of developing much larger amounts of usable energy through nuclear fission and fusion. A great deal of work is being done toward the harnessing of the nuclear energy produced by fissionable materials. But the greatest hope lies in nuclear fusion, the fuel for which is available in great abundance in the water of the sea.

Given time, there is every reason to believe that the necessary techniques for nuclear fusion will be developed and that inexhaustible supplies of energy can be placed at the disposal of all the peoples of Earth. The primary problem then will be one of relative costs per unit of energy that is made available for use. The competition is between the chemical energy stored in plants and their products, both presently and in the past; that available from harnessing the wasted sunshine of the desert; that which can be developed from falling water, winds, and waves; and the nuclear energy that can be produced.

Except for Mars, there is little reason to believe that any of the planets of the solar system other than Earth will support a great amount of vegetation. Some people are of the opinion that Moon, a satellite revolving around Earth just as Earth revolves around Sun, has some effect on Earth's vegetation. Many farmers are of the opinion that crops should be planted in a certain phase of Moon. Others are equally certain that this is merely an old superstition that persists in spite of the lack of exact evidence to support it.

Moon has a diameter of 2,100 miles and it revolves in its orbit at an average distance of 240,000 miles from Earth. The temperature of Moon varies between 215°F. in the light and minus 250°F. in the darkness. It is not a direct source of light, but it does serve as a reflector for the light of Sun. However, the quantity of Sun's light that is reflected back to Earth by Moon is not believed to be sufficient to affect plants, even in relation to the length-of-day factor. There is no evidence of life on Moon. But Moon is largely responsible for the tides that come and go as it revolves around Earth. And possibly Moon may have some corresponding influence on the vegetation of Earth as well.

There rolls the deep where grew the tree.
O Earth what changes hast thou seen!
There where the long street roars, hath been
The stillness of the central sea.
The hills are shadows, and they flow
From form to form and nothing stands;
They melt like mists, the solid lands,
Like clouds they shape themselves and go.

—TENNYSON

Chapter Nine
SALTS OF ANCIENT SEAS

THE vast seas that cover nearly three-quarters of the surface of Earth are of great interest to man and serve him in many useful ways. But the seas here under consideration are the ones Tennyson had in mind when he wrote: "There where the long street roars, hath been the stillness of the central sea." Such seas no longer exist as seas. All that remains of them are the salt deposits that were left behind after the water in which the salts had been dissolved had all evaporated. This occurred so long ago that the salt deposits are now buried under great depths of rock, soil, and drift and they are often difficult to locate. But many of them have been found at various places over the earth, often several thousand feet beneath the present land surface.

What are these salts? By far the most abundant one is limestone, a rock out of which many beautiful buildings have been built. Ordinarily, one does not think of limestone as a salt, but it is. A salt is a combination of an alkaline substance with an acid. In limestone the alkali was lime, a combination of calcium and oxygen. The acid was carbonic, which is carbon dioxide gas dissolved in water. When these two substances joined, calcium carbonate, a salt, was produced, with water as a by-product. And when this calcium carbonate settled out of the sea water, fell to the bottom of the sea, and solidified, it became limestone.

The greater part of what is now dry land has had a long and varied history at the bottom of the sea, abundant evidence of which has been uncovered in boring for water, gas, and petroleum. But more specific information on this point has been obtained by simpler means. Thus the needed evidence is quite apparent in the rocks that are exposed along the sides of deep canyons through which rivers have carved their courses. It is found in abundance in locations where deep excavations have been made by man while building highways, railroads, tunnels, and tall buildings. And much additional evidence is at hand where quarrying and mining operations are underway.

About 75 per cent of the land area of Earth is underlain with limestone, sandstone, and shale—sedimentary rocks that were formed by solidification of deposits laid down on the bottoms of ancient seas. Subsequently they were shoved up above sea level to become dry land. But of these three classes of rocks, only limestone is a salt. The sandstone and shale are made up of fragments of rocks and of the clay derived from their disintegration; they were never a part of the salts that were dissolved in the sea water. Limestone, on the other hand, is a highly important salt in the mineral economy of Earth. Its calcium is a necessary constituent of the cell walls of plants, which could not develop in stable form without it. The bones of animals and of man are made up almost entirely of calcium that has been joined to phosphoric acid to form another salt—calcium phosphate.

All the calcium on Earth, whether in limestone or in any other form, came entirely from igneous rocks that originally covered the face of the earth when it cooled down to become a solid crust. The calcium and the other mineral elements found in sea water were dissolved out of these original rocks by the rain water, leaving a residue of insoluble clay. The water that dissolved them found its way down the rivers and out to sea. Meanwhile the calcium had been joined to the carbonic acid of the atmosphere to form calcium carbonate. Such large amouts of this salt eventually accumulated in the sea that the water became saturated with it, causing it to separate out and drop to the bottom.

Part of the calcium carbonate in the sea water was used by the shell-forming animals of the sea, the most notable being coral. This coral grew abundantly, leaving its shell deposits behind to be added to the other calcium carbonate deposits. When these deposits had solidified to become limestone and had been shoved up out of the sea by gigantic subterranean forces, they existed largely in deep horizontal layers, or strata. And these strata are frequently exposed naturally and by excavations, where they can be studied in detail.

Most limestone contains some magnesium carbonate, another salt. The magnesium was also dissolved out of the original igneous rock. In combination with oxygen, it is known as magnesia. And this was also joined to carbonic acid, with water as a by-product. If the percentage of magnesium carbonate in limestone is quite large, the stone is known as dolomite. Dolomitic limestone dissolves in water much more slowly than calcitic limestone.

The most far-reaching submergence of the North American continent was during the Cretaceous period, about 100 million years ago. During that period the sea invaded the continent northward from what is now the Gulf of Mexico, gradually spreading out over the interior of the United States and extending as far north as Hudson Bay. It expanded east and west over an area more than one thousand miles in width. And during that period tremendous deposits of calcium and magnesium carbonates were laid down and consolidated into limestone on the floor of this vast inland sea.

During that same period, covering some 75 million years, the sea also invaded large areas of South America, Europe, North Africa, and Asia. And in these countries also large deposits of calcium and magnesium carbonates were deposited and solidified into limestone that was later pushed up above the sea to become dry land.

When one examines the strata of limestone that are exposed from place to place he often finds other strata of sandstone and shale alternating with those of limestone. Sometimes the layers of limestone will be repeated several times, often to great depth in each case with sandstone and shale in between. This means merely that the bottom of the sea was rising and sinking during that period of deposition, the limestone being laid down when the sea was the deepest and the sandstone when it was shallowest.

If nothing happened subsequently to interfere with the position of these layers of sedimentary rocks except for their gradually being elevated above the level of the sea, they will be found lying in a nearly horizontal plane. But if some great subterranean disturbance occurred, such as happens when mountain ranges are shoved up above the surrounding areas, these layers of stone may be at a steep angle from the horizontal. At some points they may be nearly vertical.

Where limestone constituted the surface layer of such an exposed deposit of rocks when they emerged from the sea, it disintegrated quite rapidly to form soil. Its calcium and magnesium were again dissolved by the rain and carried out to sea. Thus it appears quite probable that a given molecule of calcium or magnesium carbonate may have been in the sea, out on the dry land, and back again in the sea time after time during the long history of Earth.

Although limestone appears to be insoluble in water, it gradually dissolves in it. Given adequate time, of which there was no lack, the limestone gradually disappeared from the face of Earth, leaving only its impurities behind in the form of soil. These impurities were almost entirely sand and clay, with some associated organic matter.

If the limestone was nearly pure calcium and magnesium carbonate, a depth of as much as forty feet of it may have been required to yield one foot of soil, the other thirty-nine feet of material having been dissolved and carried away. A deep deposit of limestone was required to leave three or four feet of soil behind. What is often termed a "limestone soil" may contain only mere traces of limestone. And even these traces will disappear in time if the land is put under cultivation.

But if a deposit of limestone still remains beneath the soil, this serves a useful purpose to any plants growing on the land. The vertical and horizontal cracks that are common in limestone provide excellent drainage so that excess water does not accumulate. Consequently, plant roots can grow down deeply through not only the entire depth of soil but on down into the underlying limestone as well. It is for this reason that limestone soils are of such importance for growing alfalfa in humid regions. Alfalfa is a lime-loving legume that sends its roots down deeper into the limestone each successive year of growth.

The importance of limestone lies not only in the productivity of the soil that is developed from it but in its value for overcoming acid-soil conditions that tend to develop in areas subject to heavy rainfall—a particularly troublesome problem in the high-rainfall regions of the eastern United States and in central and northern Europe.

Virtually all the land east of the Mississippi River is covered with soil that needs liming from time to time to overcome the acidity that tends to develop in it. Some crops, including most legumes and vegetables, are very sensitive to acid-soil conditions. The agriculture of the southern states, however, is essentially an acid-soil system. Many of the crops that are being grown, including cotton, peanuts, lespedeza, and watermelons, do not respond markedly to liming the soil on which they grow.

Yet, by and large, all acid soils, including those of the southern states, require liming from time to time if farmed intensively for high acre yields. This is especially true if liberal use is being made of nitrogen fertilizers, one unfortunate result of which is the release of nitric acid, the end-product of the activities of the nitrifying bacteria that act on these fertilizers. Unless the soil contains lime, this process, known as nitrification, is slowed down by the accumulated nitric acid to the disadvantage of the crop. Where lime is present, the end-product is neutral nitrate of lime, which is highly effective in increasing the growth rate of plants.

In preparing limestone rock for use on the land as an acid-soil corrective, it must either be pulverized or burned to a fine powder. Most of the limestone used by farmers is pulverized, often to such fineness that the particles will pass through a one-hundred-mesh screen. Such a screen has ten thousand openings per square inch. When a limestone product of this fineness is applied to the land and thoroughly mixed with the soil it reacts quickly to neutralize any acid that may be present in the soil.

This neutralization process is one in which the calcium of

the limestone replaces the acid hydrogen that is attached to the particles of acid soils. As a result, water is produced and the carbon dioxide of the limestone is released back into the atmosphere from which it originally came. This evolution of carbon dioxide gas is seldom observed in the soil but it can readily be seen if one pours a few drops of hydrochloric acid on a piece of limestone. In fact, this is an easy method of distinguishing limestone from other kinds of rock closely resembling it.

Sales of agricultural liming materials in the United States are nearly 20 million tons a year, most of which are pulverized limestone. But some of the limestone is burned and the resulting product is hydrated by the addition of a small amount of water to form a finely divided product that is quickly effective when applied to the soil. The rate of application of liming materials is usually from one to two tons an acre. A little calculation soon reveals that much larger tonnages of agricultural limestone than are now being used could undoubtedly be applied to advantage to the farmed and grazed land in the eastern half of the United States.

Great masses of limestone rock, many times weighing tons, are often found lying out in the fields in areas where the soil was derived from limestone. This applies even in regions where one would think the stone would have been dissolved and carried away. Just how these boulders escaped the dissolving action of the rain water is not clear, but they were probably protected by a cover of some other less soluble kind of sedimentary rock, such as sandstone or shale.

In any event, these limestone boulders are likely to remain where they are for a long time, as measured by the life of man, continuing to be a great nuisance to farming the land. The present slowness of solution of these rocks is due largely to their lying on top the soil rather than being buried in it. They expose only a relatively limited surface area to the solvent action of the rain, whereas they would soon disappear if pulverized and mixed with the soil.

Potholes are characteristic of land that is underlain with deep deposits of limestone. These develop as a result of larger-than-usual openings in the underlying limestone through which more than the normal amount of water percolates. Thus the dissolving rate of the limestone is speeded up at these locations. Occasionally, the thin surface layer of soil and rock that remains over the top of such an underground opening will give way during a period of heavy rainfall, leaving a deep hole in the field. The immediate cause for this may be the passage of a heavy animal or a tractor over the spot. Farm buildings have been known to fall into such holes, and the water of long-established lakes and ponds has occasionally disappeared overnight into such underground openings.

The Mammoth Cave of Kentucky, which covers an area about ten miles in diameter and has over 150 miles of subterranean passageways, is an excellent example of the type cavern that can be carved out of limestone by the flow of water over long periods of time. Water, dripping slowly from the ceiling of the cavern and evaporating, has deposited its load of dissolved lime to form stalactites that have grown downward from the ceiling or stalagmites that have grown upward from the floor.

The Carlsbad Caverns of New Mexico provide another interesting example. They have three levels at depths of 750, 900, and 1,300 feet below the surface, providing homes for millions of bats. Huge deposits of the dead bodies and excreta of these flying mamals are found in these caverns and many other similar ones located in that part of the United States and down into Mexico. Large tonnages of this material are processed for use as fertilizer, being sold under the name of guano.

Phosphate rock is another sea-derived deposit of importance

equal to or greater than that of limestone. In this case the calcium is joined to phosphoric rather than carbonic acid. Phosphate rock is the most important source of phosphorus, an element required by all living things and in especially large quantities by animals and man.

Many soils, and the vegetation growing on them, have a low content of phosphorus. And much phosphorus is lost from the land by the sale of grain, milk, and livestock in which this element tends to concentrate. In overcoming deficiencies of phosphorus, whether natural or induced, use was once largely made of pulverized bones, the only known source of the element of any importance at that time. Some idea of the esteem in which bones were once held as a soil amendment can be obtained from a statement made by Justus von Liebig, the world-famous German chemist of the 1840's. He said: "England is robbing all other countries of the condition of their fertility. Already in her eagerness for bones she has turned up the battlefields of Leipsic, of Waterloo, and of the Crimea; already from the Catacombs of Sicily she has carried away the skeletons of many successive generations. Annually she removes from the shores of other countries to her own use the manurial equivalent of three millions and a half of men whom she takes from us the means of supporting and squanders down her sewers to the sea. Like a vampire, she hangs upon the neck of Europe—nay of the entire world—and sucks the heartblood of nations without a thought of justice toward them, without a shadow of lasting advantage to herself."

Liebig's statement was made long before the discovery in 1881 of the large deposits of phosphate rock in Florida. Subsequently, other deposits were found in South Carolina, Tennessee, and Arkansas. And, still later, much larger deposits were located in Montana, Idaho, Utah, and Nevada. The total workable deposits of phosphate rock in the United States are estimated at some 14 billion tons.

Phosphate rock is quite similar in composition to the bones of animals. Consequently, when these discoveries were made it soon became apparent that the need for collecting bones no longer existed. As long as they were available as packing house by-products they were used for fertilizer purposes. But the demand for phosphates was much greater than could be met by the use of bones. Soon, most of the phosphate needs of the world were being met from these phosphate rock deposits.

Eventually, other large deposits of phosphate rock were found in Morocco, and still others in Tunisia, Algeria, Russia, and certain islands of the sea. The known deposits of phosphate rock the world over are estimated at 45 billion tons, which should be sufficient to meet all the needs of man for several thousand years. But these tonnages are small indeed in comparison with those of limestone. And many countries have no deposits of phosphate rock of any important significance.

It is generally believed that the phosphorus in phosphate rock was derived from calcium phosphate accumulations in the skeletons of sea animals over many millions of years. The deposits thus developed were associated with those of limestone, and in the same locations. When the joint deposits of calcium phosphate and calcium carbonate were eventually elevated above the level of the sea, a phosphate-concentrating process set in. As the more soluble calcium carbonate was dissolved and carried away by the drainage waters, the calcium phosphate, being virtually insoluble in water, remained behind to form the now nearly pure deposits of phosphate rock.

Phosphate rock, like limestone, can be pulverized and applied to soils in need of it to great advantage. But since it is much less soluble than limestone, it must be much more finely pulverized if it is to serve a very useful purpose. This is merely a means of exposing much more surface to the solvent action of soil water and plant roots. Much of the phosphate rock that is now being sold for use on the land is made to pass a three-hundred-mesh screen having ninety thousand openings per square inch. This is being done on a large scale, the pulverized product being sold under the name of "rock phosphate."

But a much larger part of the phosphate rock that is being used for fertilizer purposes is made more soluble in water by treatment with sulfuric acid. The resulting superphosphate is a popular fertilizer material. The phosphate part of the superphosphate will dissolve readily in water, leaving a relatively insoluble residue of calcium sulfate, another salt, behind.

Limestone and phosphate rock are the best-known examples of substances that were dissolved in the sea water, used by the animal life of the sea, and finally left behind as deposits on the bottom of the sea. But the residue that remains where sea water is evaporated to dryness, as when an arm of the sea is cut off from the main body of water, is quite different from limestone and phosphate rock. This residue is made up mostly of sodium chloride, known as common salt. But it also contains a variety of other salts, consisting mostly of chlorides and sulfates of calcium, magnesium, and potassium.

Fortunately for man, great arms of the sea were isolated from it by barriers of rock that were shoved up around them. The sea water behind these natural dams began to lose its water by evaporation at a more rapid rate than it was renewed by rain. With increasing concentration of these salts, even though they were more readily soluble than calcium carbonate or calcium phosphate, they reached a point of saturation and began separating out of solution and falling to the bottom.

These happenings were frequently long-drawn-out. Tides and winds poured more sea water into these isolated seas over millions of years. When in due time, these inland seas were completely severed from the main body of water and all the water in them had evaporated, only the dry salts remained. These salt-covered inland sea bottoms were subsequently filled in with sand and soil from surrounding areas so that the whole area was brought up to the level of the land round about.

In separating from the sea water as it became ever more concentrated by evaporation, the several salts tended to be deposited at different times. Consequently, they exist in separate layers of various thicknesses. Thus in mining operations it is possible to go down to the level of the particular salt desired and bring it to the surface in virtually pure form.

For many years the largest deposit of such stratified sea salts then known was located at Stassfurt, Germany. Going downward from the surface, a layer of soil and drift of about 25 feet was first encountered. Next were considerable depths of shales, sandstones, and unconsolidated clays. Below this was a relatively shallow layer of common salt, a deposit of 75 to 250 feet of calcium sulfate, and then a layer of salt-clay having a thickness of 30 to 50 feet. Under the salt-clay was a layer of beautifully colored carnallite, a highly important source of potassium for fertilizer purposes, with a thickness of from 50 to 100 feet. Finally, there were successive layers of magnesium sulfate, another potassium salt called polyhalite, common salt, and calcium sulfate, extending downward an additional 300 to 3,000 feet.

The original exploitation of these Stassfurt salt deposits grew out of some new concepts developed by Justus von Liebig in a series of lectures presented in London in 1840 before the British Association for the Advancement of Science. In these lectures Liebig outlined what has since become known as the "mineral theory" of plant nutrition. This theory was that plants require only inorganic materials for the construction of the organic matter of which they are made. In other words, plants need carbon dioxide of the air and nitrate, mineral elements, and water from the soil to grow to full size and fruitfulness.

Before Liebig's time, the food of plants was believed to be soil organic matter. But Liebig pointed out that plants had to exist before there was any organic matter. And he showed that before soil organic matter could be used by plants it had first to be broken down into the original air, water, and mineral constituents by the soil microbes. Although Liebig's concepts were essentially correct, it is now known that small quantities of already synthesized organic substances may be absorbed by plant roots from the soil organic matter, sometimes to very good effect.

The ashes of plants provide the clue to the kinds and quantities of mineral elements required from the soil. When these were examined, it was found that plants required more than a dozen such elements. And all of these elements were found to be present in the salt deposits that were left behind when sea water was evaporated to dryness. Of these salts, those of potassium were shown to be of greatest importance as supplements to pulverized limestone and acidulated phosphate rock.

It was on this basis that the salts of the Stassfurt mines were first exploited and the fertilizer industry got under way. Up to the beginning of World War I, virtually every country on Earth was dependent on these mines for their supplies of potassium salts, the best known being potassium chloride, a derivative of carnallite and commonly known to the trade as muriate of potash. But when ocean-going vessels between Germany and the rest of the world were blockaded during that war, it became necessary to search for potassium salt deposits in other places.

It was believed that potassium salts would be found farther down in Earth below the deposits of common salt that were then being worked in New York, Michigan, Kansas, and Louisiana. But this did not prove to be true. In some manner these common salt deposits had been separated from the other sea salts with which they had been originally associated.

Quite large deposits of potassium and other salts similar to those of Stassfurt were eventually located near Carlsbad, New Mexico, and these have since been worked on an ever increasing scale. More recently large deposits of potassium-bearing sea salts, much larger than those at Stassfurt, have been discovered less than a mile below the surface in the province of Saskatchewan, Canada. Other important potassium salt deposits have been found near Mulhouse, France and Barcelona, Spain and in the vicinity of the Caspian Sea. The extremely salty waters of the Dead Sea and those of Searles Lake, California are also being worked for potassium salts.

The salt deposits in Searles Lake are quite similar to those found on the surface of the alkaline and saline soils of the arid regions of the United States and elsewhere. These salts include not only the calcium and magnesium carbonates of which limestones are made but a considerable variety of other more soluble and, therefore, more troublesome salts, such as are found dissolved in sea water—troublesome not only because of their excessive amounts and high degree of solubility but because of their alkalinity as well.

Plants grow best in soils that are near the neutral point, neither acid nor alkaline. Overcoming the alkalinity and high concentrations of soluble salts in arid regions is a much more difficult problem than that of overcoming the acidity and lack of available mineral nutrients in regions of heavy rainfall. About the only means of getting rid of the excess salts that cause trouble in irrigated arid areas is that of using extra irrigation water to dissolve them out of the soil and carry them away. But the scarcity of water for irrigation in these regions prevents the use of as much water for this purpose as would be desirable.

Soluble salts have a tendency to rise to the surface in irrigated arid areas and to form a white incrustation on top the soil. In some places farmers have resorted to use of large moldboard plows by which these surface deposits can be buried to a depth of four or five feet, temporarily removing them from the root zones of plants. But eventually they find their way back to the surface. In other places large tonnages of gypsum are applied to alkaline soils for corrective purposes, tending to lower the solubility of some of the excess salts and to reduce the alkalinity.

The agricultural limestone and fertilizer industries are engaged almost entirely in quarrying, mining, and processing sea salts from land deposits and in developing soluble nitrogen salts from the nitrogen gas of the atmosphere. All of these are applied to the soil for replacement purposes, particularly in the high-rainfall areas of the earth. Some 43 million tons of limestone and fertilizer are now being applied annually to the farmlands of the United States, and world consumption is about ten times that amount.

The agricultural limestone industry has for its primary purpose the pulverization and sale of enough limestone to neutralize the acids in the soils of the high-rainfall regions. But in so doing it also supplies calcium and magnesium, two essential mineral nutrients for plants. The fertilizer industry is designed primarly for supplying the extra nitrogen, phosphorus, and potassium required to replace the quantities of these elements lost from the soil in drainage waters and by crop removal, as well as required to meet the needs for higher acre yields of crops. But many fertilizers also contain important amounts of sulfur, another essential mineral nutrient.

A considerable number of other mineral nutrients are required only in traces by plants and by the animals that feed on them. Consequently, a great deal of study has gone into the problem of finding out how large are the quantities of these trace elements required and the extent to which soils are able to supply them. Salts of many of these elements, including those of manganese, zinc, copper, iron, boron, and molybdenum, are now being added to the ordinary fertilizers or applied separately in many parts of the earth. And cobalt, iodine and fluorine, trace elements needed by animals but not by plants, are frequently supplied also by way of the soil and its crop.

One of the important reasons why animal manures, composts, guanos, and packing house wastes have long been such popular fertilizers is that they, being the refuse of plants and animals, contain all the elements plants and animals require. But the quantities of these organic fertilizers are insufficient to meet the ever growing needs of agriculture. As a result, larger tonnages of sea salts are being used as supplements. By the joint use of organic fertilizers and sea salts an abundance of mineral-rich foodstuffs can be assured.

Sea water itself could very well be used as a source of all the mineral nutrients required by plants. From time to time the sea overflows farm lands some distance removed from its shores, the first result being the injury or death of most of the vegetation because of excessive concentration of salts in the water. But after the rains have washed out the excess salts, particularly the sodium chloride, the land again becomes productive, often much more productive than it was originally. Some of the richest soil on Earth is that covering the land that has been reclaimed from the sea in Holland.

When the time arrives that large quantities of water are being taken from the sea for purification for industrial, agricultural, and domestic purposes, the large quantities of salts separated from this water may find considerable use as supplements to the standard liming and fertilizing materials. The large tonnages of similar salts that have been piled up on the desert as by-products in the purification of Chilean nitrate are under study from this point of view.

A common thing is a grass blade small
Crushed by the feet that pass.
But all the dwarfs and giants tall
Working 'til doomsday shadows fall
Can't make a blade of grass.

—JULIUS STEARNS CUTLER

Chapter Ten

A BLADE OF GRASS

SOIL, air, rain, and Sun supply all the essentials for the growing of a blade of grass. But they do not explain the grass. For they are inanimate things, whereas grass is a living, growing, reproducing entity. It began with a tiny seed in which was enclosed a spark of life. And from this humble beginning the grass got its start, grew, and flourished. If it was an annual grass it developed seed and dropped them back on the land before it died, but if it was a perennial type it may have spread in all directions from the main plant without benefit of seed.

Wherever one goes, grass was there before him. Grass carpets vast areas of the earth's surface. And whenever land is laid bare by the hand of man, grass is standing by, ready to spring into action, spread over the area, and erase the scars. "Grass is the forgiveness of Nature—her constant benediction," wrote John J. Ingalls. "Fields trampled with battle, saturated with blood, torn with ruts of cannon grow green again with grass, and carnage is forgotten. Forests decay, harvests perish, flowers vanish, but grass is immortal."

Grass is an outgrowth of a long evolutionary process that began with a mere microbe more than one billion years ago. It has within itself not only a spark of life but a set of genes that enable it to grow and reproduce itself. It is the seat of an evolutionary process by which it came into being and through which it has continued to develop ever since. Accordingly, there are a great many species of grass arising from the need to be able to survive under the many different environments of Earth, with particular reference to their soils and climates.

The green in grass is due to many millions of molecules of chlorophyll that are present in every square inch of leaf area. This chlorophyll has the peculiar capacity of being able to absorb the transient light energy of the sun and to transform it into stored chemical energy in the form of the organic substances produced by the plant out of soil, air, and water. This stored chemical energy in green plants can be rapidly released if the grass is dried and burned. It is more slowly released if the grass is consumed as feed. And it is released still more slowly if the grass or its waste products are worked into the soil and are decomposed by its microbial population.

To many people, grass means mostly the green swards of lawns, roadsides, parks, and golf courses. To others it means the millions of acres of grazing lands that support the livestock—mainly sheep and cattle—of Earth. To many others it means the beautiful meadows that are harvested for hay or silage to carry livestock through the winter months. And to still others grass means all the forage crops, including both the true grasses and the legumes, for whatever purpose they may be grown.

But the grass family includes many more species than these. All the important small grains, including wheat, oats, barley, rye, and millet, are members of the grass family. Rice, the staff of life to the peoples of the Orient, is another extremely important grass, which bids fair to become even more important with time. And sugar cane, the world's most important sucrose-producing crop, is a grass.

Maize, or Indian corn, which first came to world attention with its discovery in the Americas, its home grounds, is also a grass. The word "corn" has come to mean the principal grain crop of a country: in England it is wheat; in Scotland, oats; and in Asia, rice. In the United States, maize, the principal grain crop of the Indians, came to be a highly prized crop by the white man. In due time it became such an important part of the agricultural economy of the New World that it won the title of "corn."

"In Iowa where the tall corn grows, in Ohio and Illinois, in Indiana, Kansas, and Nebraska, in Minnesota and Dakota, in Georgia where more acres grow corn than grow cotton, in Maine and California, in Michigan, Kentucky, Tennessee, Alabama, and Louisiana—in every state in the Union," wrote Howard Zahnizer, "the farmers of America plant corn to rise into the rank and file of the greatest crop that man has yet mobilized."

A great deal is known about the evolution of the corn plant, beginning with the tiny cobs that were turned up in excavating the accumulations of trash in a once-inhabited Indian rock shelter in New Mexico. By using the now widely employed radiocarbon dating process, these cobs, which had a length of only about one-half inch, were found to be about 5,600 years old. The ears of corn one now sees by the millions in the fields of this crop over the United States are often more than one foot in length. The evolutionary selection and breeding processes that have operated since these early days have developed a truly amazing crop that is capable of yielding over three-hundred bushels of shelled grain, each weighing fifty-six pounds, per acre.

Grass has been selected to represent not only its own highly diverse family of plants but all the other green plants that play such important parts in the welfare of man. These many different kinds of green plants have become so efficient in synthesizing organic products out of purely inorganic materials that they have long since displaced virtually all the original nonchlorophyll microbes in this capacity. This means that green plants now provide not only the feed and food required by animals and man but the nourishment needed by the countless millions of microbes that inhabit every handful of good soil the world over. These green plants synthesize their own substance, year after year, using the same raw materials over and over again in the process. This is an excellent example of the economy of nature, which has much more importance to man than most people realize.

In their younger stages of growth, green plants are made up mostly of loosely bound water that can readily be driven off into the air when the plants are dried under a clear sky or in an oven. But their content of this essentially free water is gradually reduced as maturity approaches, when they consist mostly of starch, cellulose, oil, and protein, all highly concentrated forms of chemical energy. And large quantities of plant-stored energy from a far distant past are found preserved in such natural fuels as coal, petroleum, and natural gas.

The exact method by which light energy is transformed into chemical energy is something a great many scientists would like to be able to explain. Some of them are searching for the clue merely for the sake of adding to the sum of human knowledge. Others are greatly interested because of the possibility of putting this process into operation on a factory scale. Eventually, some scientist will probably find the answer.

Some plants, notably sugar cane and sugar beets, synthesize and store large amounts of sucrose, the common table sugar. The grasses, grain crops, and tubers, such as the potato, are mostly starch producers. Starch can readily be changed into glucose, a simple sugar of the type contained in the sirup that is made from corn, by factory procedures. Cotton, hemp, flax, and jute plants are manufacturers of cellulose fibers, as are trees. The legume seeds, such as peas and beans, have high contents of protein. Cottonseed, flaxseed and soybeans are particularly valuable because of their high contents of both protein and oil. Tomatoes, melons, and vegetables are mostly water.

Many plants are valued for the highly peculiar properties they possess. Tobacco, tea, coffee, and cacao are favorably regarded because of their stimulatory effects arising from their relatively high content of particular alkaloids. Large numbers of herbs are grown for their delightful aromas and flavoring properties. Other plants are noted for their production of toxic substances, some of which are made use of for the control of insects. Alkaloids of other plants have medicinal values.

Green plants also produce and contain at maturity appreciable quantities of a great variety of miscellaneous organic substances that play highly important roles in the nutrition of animals and man. Among these are the many different but highly essential vitamins that are required by all animal life and that are present in such small quantities that knowledge of their presence and importance came only after many years of study on the part of biochemists and nutritionists. And the enzymes, hormones, and many different esters in plants play important parts in nutrition and in taste appeal to man.

These variations in the natures and amounts of the many organic compounds synthesized by the several species and varieties of plants give them their characteristic odors and flavors, their special stimulatory or medicinal properties, or their particular nutritional or other use values. The health of man is governed largely by how well he chooses from among the many foods at his disposal in the formulation of his diet, which should contain all the essential nutrients in adequate and balanced proportions. When given free choice animals appear to have a greater capacity to choose advantageously than does the uneducated man.

Taste appeal is as important as nutritional value to most people. Thus wheat does not taste like maize. Apples are readily distinguishable from pears. Peanuts have little resemblance to pecans. Watermelons are quite different from cantaloups. Tea and coffee have essentially the same stimulatory effects on man, but they taste quite differently to him. And tobacco provides an entirely different and unique type of pleasure for those who enjoy it.

Shades of green in plants are characteristic for the several species and varieties. They vary from blue-green to green-yellow, with all the gradations in between. It is this variety of greens that makes the summer landscape so attractive. These differences in shades of green are apparent in the several grasses, grain crops, and vegetables in the farmers' fields, in the flowers and shrubs about the house and yard, and in the bushes and trees throughout the parks and forests.

When the green fades out in the fall of the year and the highly decorative yellows and reds take their places, winter is not far ahead. Only the evergreens stand out in marked contrast to the autumn colors and to the winter snow that covers the land of the colder climates. But with the first warm days at winter's end, the grasses and decidous plants develop new life and the green quickly comes back again as a welcome harbinger of another spring, with the renewed hope and faith that come with it.

The primary urge of green plants is that of meeting their own needs for growth and reproduction. They are not concerned with the needs of man, the animals on which he depends, or the scavenger microbes that harbor in the soil. Animals, insects, and parasitic microbes have inserted themselves into the green plants' world. And man looks upon green plants as his to bring under control, to domesticate, to redesign, and to use in conformity with his own needs and desires. Within limits, green plants are as clay in the geneticist's hands.

The green plants one now sees as he drives across the country are, for the most part, not those that were there originally. When the first white man arrived in the United States, virtually all the land east of the Mississippi River and much of that in the first north-and-south line of states west of it was covered with dense forest. Here and there were burned-over areas and fields of corn and other food crops. But a squirrel could have gone from Maine to Louisiana without touching the ground, merely by leaping from one giant forest tree to the next.

To the northeast and southwest evergreens predominated, with deciduous forests in between. In the northern forests pine, spruce, and hemlock were the principal species. But large numbers of sugar maple, beech, birch, elm, ash, basswood, and red oak were found among the evergreens. In the central portion of this forested region, from New York to Indiana and from Virginia to Arkansas, broadleaf deciduous species of trees prevailed, among which were the hickory, black cherry, black walnut, gum, ash, maple, tulip poplar, and many varieties of oak. In the southern states the longleaf, shortleaf, loblolly, and slash pines were dominant. But interspersed among these evergreen were a great variety of deciduous trees, including the cypress, cottonwood, tupelo, tulip poplar, live oak, and magnolia. Pecan trees grew in the south central area and palms flourished in the far south.

Beyond these forested lands to the west, beginning in northern Indiana and widening across Illinois and Iowa, were the open prairies with their tall grasses, of which the highly prized bluestems were the dominant species. Farther west across the Great Plains, the short grasses, including the well-known gramas and buffalo grass, predominated. Then came the near-deserts and deserts farther west, with their great variety of dry-land grasses, shrubs, herbs, and cacti. Finally, the tallest forest trees in America entered the picture along the Pacific Coast. The world's heaviest stands of tall timber, including the famous Douglas firs and the thousand-year-old sequoias, were there. And many other evergreens, such as the white ponderosa pine, the hemlock, the fir, the cedar, and the spruce, were native to that region.

Now, some 350 years later, little of the virgin forest remains. The trees that are now growing in the forested areas are generally second-growth types, but with ever increasing acreages of planted trees, mostly evergreens. Cultivated crops and grasses have replaced the forests and the native grasses over large acreages of land. The grasses east of the Mississippi River, and the legumes associated with them, are largely introduced species brought to this country by the pioneers from Europe.

Nearly 400 million acres of once forested, grassed and desert lands are now being used for growing feed, food, and fiber crops. About 100 million more acres have been taken over for cities and towns, highways and railroads, airports and parks, wildlife preserves, and national defense purposes. And very large acreages of grazing land no longer contain any of the original native grasses.

Forests and woodlands are being confined more and more to

hilly and mountainous lands, stony and wet lands, and lands that are too sandy to support the more demanding types of vegetation. Farmers have monopolized the best land—that which is level, well-drained, and naturally productive—for growing the kinds of crops they can use and sell. It is highly important that as much as possible of this good agricultural land be protected against encroachment by those whose interests are in industrial and suburban development rather than in agriculture.

Forests are being brought under control, protected from fire, and improved by man. A great deal of attention is being paid to replacing the original types of forest trees with more productive species. Selection and breeding are being applied to trees, as it has long been applied to grains, clovers, fiber crops, vegetables, and fruits. Fertilizers are finding their way into the management program for forests that are being used in pulp and lumber production.

The same applies to the natural grasses, which are being rapidly replaced by domesticated species that have been selected and bred for higher acre yields of higher-quality forage. A great deal of attention is being given to the range grasses of which many varieties are available for improvement by selection and breeding. Greater effort is being put into the production of more seed of improved varieties and into the protection of new seedings until the young grass gets well under way.

A close inspection of the most important crop plants of the United States mainland provides a means of sharpening one's appreciation of the highly important parts that are played by green plants in the well-being and enjoyment of man. It aids in understanding why it is so essential that a great deal more thought and effort be directed toward the development and protection of plants. And it makes it evident that improvement of soil conditions is imperative so that feed, food, and fiber crops can be grown to not only higher acre yields but to higher quality of produce in relation to the uses to which they are to be put.

In the northeastern part of the United States one is impressed by the large acreages that are being devoted to grass and clover for hay and pasture purposes, primarily for dairy cows. But one also sees large fields of potatoes, vegetables, and small grains, as well as sizeable acreages of tobacco, many acres of which are grown under tents. Apple and peach orchards, embroidered with pink blossoms in the spring and red-cheeked fruits in the autumn, are widely distributed over the region.

Moving southward, the sweet potato, or yam, largely replaces the white potato. More fields of tobacco and large acreages of peanuts come into view. Cotton, with its white blossoms the first morning and pink the next, becomes a highly important crop. Out of the green bolls that replace the blossoms come the pure white fibers for use in the manufacture of clothing and the seed that have high value for oil and protein.

Hay and pasture lands still abound, but they are covered with different grasses, of which the recently developed coastal Bermuda grass is an excellent example. The red and alsike clovers and the alfalfa of the North have been largely replaced in the South by such forage legumes as lespedeza, lupines, cowpeas, and the wide-ranging kudzu vine. The brilliant color of many large fields of crimson clover in early spring is a sight long to be remembered. Acreages of small grains are not so large, but corn is still much in evidence. More beef cattle are noted and many corn- and peanut-fed hogs, the latter producing a differently flavored pork, are to be found.

Many groves of planted pecan trees enter the picture, notably in Georgia and extending westward into Texas. Tung trees, grown for the nonedible oil their nuts yield, appear in northern Florida and continue as far west as Mississippi. Citrus trees dominate the landscape over large and rapidly expanding acreages in Florida. Farther south a few groves of papayas, mangoes, and avocados appear, and occasional small plantings of pineapples and bananas. Many cabbage palms are noted in the sandy open spaces and long lines of tall imperial palms grow along the city boulevards. Spanish moss drapes gracefully from many forest trees, notably the live oaks.

One cannot forget the flame vines that grow along the fences and appear to set them on fire. Then there are the purple bougainvillaeas that climb the trees, the beautiful camellias, the bright red poinsettias, and the forests of nearly pure magnolias with their waxen white flowers. Semitropical vegetation of great variety abounds.

From Virginia southward along the Atlantic Coast and from Florida westward along the Gulf of Mexico, celery, spinach, turnip greens, other salad crops, and native American winter vegetables such as potatoes and tomatoes tend to be dominant among the intensively grown crops. Down in the Everglades of Florida a large area of once swampy black peat soil has been brought under control by man for the production of winter vegetables and sugar cane. But large acreages of semitropical forests, abounding in a great variety of wildlife, still exist.

Moving northward into the central states, the outstanding feature of the farming is the large percentage of the land that is being devoted to grain crops. Corn, used primarily for hog and cattle feed, is the dominant grain crop in Indiana, Illinois, Iowa, and Wisconsin. One drives by fields of tall corn extending for many miles along the highway. Scattered about in the corn belt are millions of acres of soybeans, a crop imported from China that has special value as a source of protein feed to supplement the starchy corn. It is also an important source of oil which, along with oil derived from cottonseed, is used in the production of margarine as a replacement for butter.

Moving westward winter wheat becomes the dominant grain

crop in Nebraska, Kansas, Oklahoma, and West Texas. Many millions of acres of waving wheat are seen and billions of bushels of grain are produced every year. Grain sorghum, a dry-land crop, tends to replace corn in the wheat belt, and larger acreages of alfalfa enter the picture. North of the corn and wheat belts, spring wheat, oats, and barley come into greater prominence, and other large acreages of alfalfa are found.

From the wheat belt westward, grazing lands for beef cattle—particularly white-faced Herefords—and for sheep dominate the agricultural landscape. Mohair goats come into prominence in southwestern Texas. To the far south, in the Río Grande Valley, early vegetables, citrus fruit, and cotton enter the picture on the irrigated land along the river. And in California other large acreages of citrus trees and cotton are found. Orchards of plums, prunes, figs, dates, and avocados are noted toward the south. Large groves of English walnuts and almonds are to be seen. Farther north many thousands of acres are devoted to grapes for wine and raisins.

Apple and pear orchards abound in Oregon and Washington. Grain, grass, and other forage crops again come into prominence in the cooler and moister region of the far Northwest. Dairying and lumbering become much more important industries. But nearby Idaho is famous for its white potatoes that are grown to phenomenal size and yields on irrigated arid land.

Side trips from the main line of travel of some three thousand miles across the United States from east to west reveal the cranberry bogs of Massachusetts, New Jersey, and Wisconsin; peppermint fields in Michigan; sugar cane plantations in Louisiana; rice fields in Arkansas, southwest Texas, and Louisiana; and beautiful purple-flowered flax in the Dakotas.

From New England westward to Ohio many groves of sugar maples are tapped every spring for the sap out of which the delectable maple sirup is made. Not far removed in Pennsylvania and West Virginia are many small fields of white-flowered buckwheat, the grain of which furnishes the flour for making delicious buckwheat pancakes.

Many varieties of beans are being grown the country over. These include the navy beans of Michigan, the kidney beans of the western states, the closely related black-eyed peas and cowpeas of the southern states, and the soybeans of the central West. Castor beans are of considerable interest. And the many acres of high quality peas for freezing and canning that are grown in Wisconsin and Minnesota merit special mention in this connection.

Plum, pear, apple, and cherry orchards are scattered over the northeastern quarter of the United States. Huckleberries grow wild over large areas and good-sized acreages of cultivated blueberries are found. In and around the cactus-covered desert and semiarid regions, large acreages of melons are seen under irrigation. Sugar beets are grown under irrigation in Colorado and Utah and without it in Michigan and Indiana. And the watermelon abounds throughout the humid south.

Many flowering trees of special interest are found from region to region. Among these are the white-flowered catalpa, the pink hawthorn of the north, the crape myrtle of the south, and the widely distributed locust. The rhododendron and mountain laurel of the cooler and moister regions of the north are replaced by the azaleas and abelias to the south. The honeysuckle abounds throughout the eastern half of the country. In Louisiana not only the kudzu plant but the purple wisteria as well climbs to the tops of the tallest trees. And, in a favorable spring, hundreds of miles of many-colored desert flowers line the roadside and spread out across the grazing land in the arid regions of the southwest, as far as the eye can see.

In many areas the countryside is decorated with acres of cultivated flowers, in full bloom in their season, that are being grown for seed and bulbs. Here and there such odd crops as safflowers and aritchokes are found. Wild sunflowers abound in Kansas, the cultivated ones appearing in many yards and gardens and, occasionally, in full fields. Mention should be made also of the wild black walnut, the butternut, and the hickory nut. The wild chestnut, which once abounded throughout the eastern half of the United States but was completely destroyed by blight, is now coming back under conditions of cultivation in blight-resistant form.

The strawberry, which is widely grown the country over, but particularly along the Atlantic Coast and in Louisiana, should not be forgotten. Then there are the blackberries, dewberries, raspberries, boysenberries and a number of other members of this group. The delicately flavored wild elderberry, the papaw, and the persimmon, as well as the cultivated quince, the apricot, and the mulberry, merit mention.

What one sees on the United States mainland is only a small part of Earth's total bounty of green plants that man has put to work in his own behalf. Other plants are dominant in other parts of the world. In eastern Europe and in Russia, rye is a highly important bread crop and sunflower seeds take the place of peanuts. Barley and oats are the preferred grains in northern Europe. Large acreages of soybeans are being grown in Manchuria for protein and oil. White potatoes have long been a dominant crop in Ireland, having been imported from their native home in America. The agricultural economy of southeast Asia is built around rice.

Among the many agricultural plants not grown commercially in the United States are the rubber, coconut palm, and mahogany trees of the tropics. Other highly important tropical plants are cacao and coffee trees, bananas, teas, spices, and vanilla beans. Bamboo is an important crop, both for food and fiber. Hemp and jute are grown on a large scale for fiber in the

Orient. Pineapples are a speciality of the Hawaiian Islands. World commerce is largely concerned with the movement of these and many other agricultural products from areas of surplus to those of scarcity.

These various forms of green-plant life are all subject to attack by diseases and insects and to competition from weeds. A great deal of time and effort is being invested in developing means of protecting crop plants against such pests. All plants are capable of being improved for man's purposes by selection and breeding, and among the many possibilities for their improvement is the development of built-in resistance to disease and insect attack.

Such techniques, however, are of little avail unless the soils on which the several crop plants are being grown are maintained in a high state of fertility. This involves not only soil and water conservation techniques that hold the soil where it is and absorb the rain where it falls but others that have for their purpose the restoration to the soil of the nitrogen and mineral nutrients lost in drainage waters and through crop removal. Special attention must be given to the use of liming materials in acid-soil areas and to means of preventing salt accumulation and the development of excess alkalinity in irrigated arid areas. The need for supplemental applications of mineral nutrients and nitrogen is general.

It is important, however, that all of us realize the significance of green plants, the contribution they make to the well-being of man, and his dependence upon them. The more primitive forms of green plants were here on the earth well in advance of the coming of man. They and their evolved forms are man's to use. But these green plants also offer a challenge in that they have the ingrown capacity for tremendous improvement in yielding ability and in quality, as measured by man's wants and needs.

The possibilities of moving farther and farther into the tropics, the deserts, and the frigid lands of the earth from the surrounding areas of more hospitable environment are very great. The boundaries of these vast areas of unused lands are not fixed. But they can expand as well as contract. And it is up to man to devise the ways and means by which ever larger acreages of these inhospitable lands are brought under control for green-plant production in such a manner as to make the developments permanent ones.

Remember, O man, that thou art dust
and to dust shalt thou return.

—LITURGICAL ADAPTION FROM GENESIS

Chapter Eleven

THE SOIL IN MAN

SOILS, by way of plants, put their marks on mankind. They vary greatly in mineral and nitrogen content from region to region, and the plants growing on them do likewise. And since plants require mineral nutrients and nitrogen in constructing their substance out of the gases of the atmosphere and the water that falls as rain, it would be expected that the organic composition of plants would also vary greatly from region to region.

Man ordinarily thinks of feed and food plants as sources of carbohydrates, oils, and proteins. Or he may think of them as sources of the necessary vitamins. At other times the esters, which give some plants their delightful flavors and aromas, or the alkaloids of other plants, that serve such a variety of stimulation and medicinal purposes, will be foremost in his mind.

But most of the soil-derived mineral nutrients in plants are just as necessary to animals and man as they are to the plants themselves. If adequate quantities of these mineral nutrients are not contained in feeds and foods, symptoms of deficiency will soon appear and serious consequences may result. Toxic mineral elements that are present in some soils and are taken up by the plants growing on them often quickly register their injurious effects.

Some one hundred different elements are contained in, on, and around Earth. Seventeen of them are known to be required by plants. Four—carbon, hydrogen, oxygen, and nitrogen—constitute about 95 per cent of the dry weight of the average plant. Derived from air and water, they are driven off as gases when plants are burned. The others, left behind in the ashes, are mineral elements that the plants obtained from the soil on which it grew. These ashes constitute about 5 per cent of the dry weight of plants. But the ash content of man is from 10 to 15 per cent of his dry weight.

Most of the soil-derived mineral nutrients required by plants are needed by animals and man as well. But one of them—boron—is not. And the traces of iodine and fluorine, that are normally taken up from the soil by the roots of plants and distributed throughout their tissues, have little or no known value to the plants themselves but are essential to animals and man.

Plants also contain considerable amounts of silicon, aluminum, and titanium, that were obtained from the soil, and lesser quantities of a great variety of other soil-derived mineral elements of no presently known nutritional value either to the plants themselves or to any very important form of animal life. There is nothing to prevent plants from absorbing these or any other mineral elements contained in the soil, whether they are useful or not. In fact, plants absorb elements that are not only poisonous to the animals that feed on them but to themselves as well.

Although only thirteen soil-derived mineral elements are known to be required by plants and only fifteen of them by animals, others are believed to have supplemental values to both plants and animals. And still others may later be found to be necessary or useful. The trace elements are needed in quantities of only a few parts per million or per billion of plant or animal substance. These small quantities present great difficulties to the chemists and biologists who are trying to find out whether they are essential to living things.

By and large, the chemical composition of the atmosphere and that of the rain out in the open country, where most of the crops are being grown, are essentially the same the world over. Such gases as may be given off by the burning of fuels in manufacturing processes and during volcanic eruptions, sometimes to the point of injuring or killing plants, or even man, in the immediate vicinity, are normally well-diluted by the gases natural to the atmosphere before they reach the large crop-growing areas that are usually well-removed from the cities.

The soil, rather than the atmosphere or the rain, is the primary variable controlling the nutritional quality, both organic and inorganic, of any given species and variety of plant. But temperature and the amount of light also affect plant quality. Also, the younger the plant the higher its content of free water. But once this water has been driven off by drying in the open air or by the use of heat, the dry matter that remains is much higher in its percentages of mineral matter and protein than that of more mature plants. As plants mature they tend to accumulate more starch and cellulose, with consequent increase in energy values and dilution of mineral and protein values.

Many questions have been raised concerning the extent to

which variations in the mineral quality of soils affect the nutritional quality of the produce of the plants growing on them. If the nutritional quality of plant produce does vary considerably from soil to soil, one would expect this to be reflected in the well-being of the people who consume the products of the several soils. And this might well apply whether the plant products were eaten as such or by way of the meat and milk produced by feeding them to livestock.

One might well ask whether the chemically quite different gray, brown, black, yellow, and red soils of Earth produce quite different plant products that are capable of putting their respective marks on mankind. If so, are these differences in nutritional values due to variations in the mineral qualities of the plants, to those in their organic qualities, or to both?

Should the nature of the soil be considered in choosing a location for growing livestock or for bringing up a family? Does it make any difference whether the wheat and rice, the apples and oranges, the potatoes and tomatoes, and the many other grains, fruits, and vegetables one eats and the water and wine one drinks came from soils that were derived from granite, sandstone, limestone, shale, or peat? Is there any dependable evidence that people from the drier regions of Earth, where soils have not been subjected to heavy leaching rains over the centuries, are physically or mentally superior to their counterparts in the high-rainfall regions? If so, would it be desirable to encourage greater interchange of foodstuffs among the peoples of the several climatic regions of Earth?

Is it important to consumers that farmers in regions of heavy rainfall, where, as a consequence, the soils are acid, lime the land on which feed and food crops are being grown? Does it make any difference to man whether the soil's supplies of mineral nutrients and nitrogen are renewed by applying composts and manures and by growing legumes rather than by the use of chemical fertilizers?

When acre yields of crops are raised to much higher levels by selection and breeding, as in the development of hybrid corn, does this result in lowering the mineral and protein values of the plant products? If so, is there any means by which this deterioration in quality can be overcome?

Should missing mineral elements needed by animals and man but not by plants be supplied by way of the soil and crops rather than as mineral supplements to the common salt that is being consumed? Would it be desirable to substitute a salt mixture containing all the essential mineral elements for the common salt that is now being consumed by animals and man? Would sea salt have worthwhile advantages in this connection?

These questions are not raised with the thought of dealing directly with them, since considerable doubt exists in the minds of most men who are primarily engaged in trying to solve these problems, and closely related ones, about which the answers should be. The thought is rather that, with these questions in mind, one should be in a much better position to think of the soil in relation to meeting the nutritional needs of man. A great many isolated facts are known that, when pieced together, aid in reaching reasonable conclusions concerning these and many other closely connected questions that are being raised. A number of such facts have been selected as being of particular interest in this connection.

The earliest civilizations came into being and reached their highest levels on the unleached soils of the semiarid and irrigated arid regions of East Asia and North Africa. Soils of limestone origin, the earth over, are highly favored for livestock production. The Bluegrass region of Kentucky, famed for its fine horses, is located on soil having a high content of calcium phosphate. The inhabitants of certain areas of Arizona are seldom troubled with tooth decay, with the extra soil fluorine receiving the credit.

In contrast, the animals and people of certain regions have suffered from deficiencies of mineral elements in the food they ate and the water they drank. Switzerland, for example, was long noted for the number of large pendant goitrous growths with which the people were troubled in many areas. Similarly, the Great Lakes region of the United States, extending westward into Montana, had a high incidence of goiter in both animals and man. These troubles are known to have been due to a deficiency of iodine, which is now being supplied as a supplement to common salt. Iodine deficiency was responsible also for the birth of many hairless pigs and calves in that region before farmers learned to make use of iodized salt.

Widespread deficiencies of phosphorus in soils and crops, with resulting troubles with livestock, have been noted in many parts of the United States, notably in Michigan, Minnesota, and Montana. In such areas the animals are badly stunted, tending to have small bones and stiffened joints. They have an abnormal appetite for any bones that may be found in the fields or around the farmstead. Bone meal is being supplied to livestock as a supplement to common salt to great advantage in these areas.

Many areas of deficiency in cobalt have been found in various parts of the world, especially in Australia and New Zealand and in New Hampshire, South Carolina, and Texas in the United States. Animals in such areas suffer from anemia; they are stunted and have low reproductive capacity. It is now common practice to add a cobalt salt to fertilizer in those areas or to mix it with the common salt that is being fed. Many of the feed producers in the dairy areas of the northeastern quarter of the United States are now adding two grams of cobalt sulfate to every ton of feed sold.

Evidence of deficiencies in iron, copper, and manganese in the diet of both children and livestock, as indicated by anemias, has been found in certain parts of Florida. Reports from Finland suggest that people living in regions of strongly acid soils are more subject to tuberculosis than those of regions where the soils are high in lime. Men who work around limestone quarries or lime-burning plants are believed to be relatively free from tuberculosis.

A great deal of trouble has been experienced in Kansas and neighboring states from what is known as "grass tetany." Similar troubles have been reported in Holland. The evidence indicates that this is due to an excess of potassium in the young green wheat or grass on which the livestock graze during the late fall and early spring months. In proportion as a plant has an abundance of potassium at its disposal it will not absorb nearly as much calcium or magnesium as it normally would. The immediate remedy has been found in injections of calcium and magnesium gluconates. Where the soils are acid—this applies to Holland but not to Kansas—dolomitic limestone, which is high in both calcium and magnesium, can be applied to the soil to good long-time effect in controlling this trouble.

The soils of the high-rainfall tropical regions tend to be low in both calcium and phosphorus and, as a result, the people eating the produce of these regions are often small in stature. Fortunately for these people, the sun, falling on their bare skins, permits the synthesis of more than normal amounts of vitamin D, a highly important aid to calcium absorption and use in bone production. The bony framework of these people is often spare from the low content of calcium and phosphorus in their diet, but their bony structures are solidly built.

The soils of certain parts of Earth contain such large quantities of particular mineral elements of the type that are highly toxic to animals and man as to be injurious and sometimes fatal to those consuming the produce of these soils. Of these elements, selenium is probably the most troublesome. This element is a serious hazard to livestock. It may be also to people if they consume only such foods as are produced locally. Yet traces of this element are required by both plants and animals.

Selenium is present in largest amounts in the vegetation of semiarid regions where the soils were derived from rocks of the Cretaceous period. These soils have not been subjected to sufficient rainfall and drainage to carry the selenium away. Such a region extends in a wide belt from inside western Canada entirely across the United States, from the Dakotas southward to Mexico City. The primary problem is that of dealing with selenium-accumulating plants, of which certain species of *Astragalus* are the most troublesome examples.

Two types of selenium injury are noted in livestock that graze on such forage. One, known as "blind staggers," has frequently led to the deaths of large numbers of migrating sheep in a very short time. The other results in the malformation and sloughing-off of the hoofs of all classes of animals.

Molybdenum, a trace element that is required in such small amounts by both plants and animals that it escaped the notice of nutritionists until quite recently, is also troublesome when in excess. Certain soils, notably some of those in California, Florida, and the British Isles, contain so much of this element in highly available form that the forage growing on them is toxic to livestock. The most readily recognized symptom of such toxicity is the serious diarrhea that results. If not remedied, the animals will die. This is another case of mineral imbalance from the plant's absorption of too much of one element at the expense of or in relation to another element. In this case a remedy is found in adding copper sulfate to the common salt that is fed.

Fluorine, an essential trace-mineral nutrient for animals

and man but not for plants, is troublesome when present in excess in feeds, foods, and water. In certain parts of the United States, notably in the drier areas of the Southwest and in the vicinity of phosphate-rock deposits, the soil and water are naturally quite high in this element. Unfortunately also, fluorine is given off as a gas into the surrounding atmosphere in a number of manufacturing processes, notably those of the aluminum and superphosphate industries. The fluorine thus evolved is brought down to Earth in rain and is absorbed by the roots of plants. It may also be absorbed through the leaves of plants.

Fluorine is an essential constituent of teeth. When the supply in feed, food, or water is inadequate, trouble is experienced with excessive tooth decay. In larger amounts, however, it becomes destructive; the teeth take on a mottled appearance, turn brown, become brittle, and tend to disintegrate. Considerable difficulty was experienced when rock phosphate, which is high in fluorine, was substituted for bone meal as a supplemental mineral feed for cattle. This difficulty is being overcome by heating the rock phosphate to high enough temperatures to drive the fluorine off into the atmosphere. Drinking water is now being fluoridated in many cities where its content is below that believed to be required for sound teeth.

The richest soils, in terms of mineral nutrients in forms that are readily available to plants, are generally found in irrigated arid regions. There the soils have not been subjected to serious leaching by heavy rainfall over long periods of time. Other mineral-rich soils are found in the wide valleys toward the mouths of great rivers. There topsoil from wide acreages upstream has been spread out over the land with each recurring flood. Such alluvial soils are deep and highly productive.

Glaciated soils, such as those that cover most of Canada, a part of the northern half of the United States, and the northern part of Europe, are also relatively rich in mineral nutrients.

The glaciers ground vast quantities of nutrient-rich rocks to a fine powder and mixed it with the underlying soil within relatively recent time, the last ice invasion having been only about eleven thousand years ago. Similarly, there are large areas of land over which deep deposits of nutrient-rich volcanic ash have been spread quite recently.

The soil-derived mineral nutrients required by plants may be conveniently divided into three groups. Phosphorus and potassium are most likely to be deficient because of their being removed by plants in largest quantities in relation to the available supplies in the soil. These, together with nitrogen, an air-derived element obtained by most plants by way of the soil, are known as the major nutrients. They are commonly supplied in extra quantities in the form of mineral fertilizers.

A second group, known as the secondary nutrients, are just as essential to plants but are not so generally deficient in soils. This group includes calcium, magnesium, and sulfur. Calcium and magnesium are most likely to be deficient in acid soils and such deficiencies are normally remedied by the use of pulverized limestone. Mineral fertilizers normally contain considerable amounts of calcium and sulfur in association with the major nutrients, and sulfur also reaches the land in industrial areas as sulfur dioxide dissolved in rainwater.

Trace elements constitute a third group of soil-derived mineral nutrients. These include iron, manganese, zinc, copper, cobalt, boron, molybdenum, selenium, and chlorine. These elements are required in quantities of only a few parts per million of the dry weight of plants. Large areas of deficiency of one or another of several of these elements are known. And it is believed that other large areas of deficiency will be found in due time.

When the mineral-nutrient needs of animals and man are considered, calcium, phosphorus, sodium, and chlorine become the major group; potassium, magnesium, and sulfur, the secondary group; and the trace elements constitute a third group. When quantities and ratios are considered, the mineral-nutrient requirements of animals and man differ materially from those of plants.

The quantities of sodium and chlorine in most of the soils of the humid regions are so small that feed and food crops contain only mere traces of these elements—traces sufficient to meet the needs of most plants but far from adequate to meet the needs of herbivorous animals and of man. They represent deficiencies that must be overcome. And, strange as it may seem, even the most ardent organic gardener who objects to the use of chemical fertilizers has no hesitancy whatever in seasoning his food with common salt, which is a purely inorganic chemical salt.

Deficiencies of trace-mineral nutrients, whether one is thinking in terms of those needed by plants, by animals, or by both, are not always caused by their being present in too-limited amounts in the soil. They may be due to the low solubility of the soil forms of these elements in water, an essential to their being absorbed by plant roots. Iron is often deficient in plants, notably in trees, notwithstanding that soils contain abundant supplies of this element. A problem often involved with iron is that it tends to form insoluble compounds inside the plant before it reaches the growing tips. The leaves of plants then turn a golden yellow and growth ceases. In trees, the mere driving of iron nails into the trunks and branches is all that is required to overcome this deficiency. But better methods are known for correcting this and other trace-element deficiencies, both in trees and all other plants.

Deficiencies of soil-derived elements required by animals but not by plants cannot be detected by any abnormalities in the appearance of the plants, but they may be readily apparent in the animals that consume the plants. In meeting the needs of farm animals, these elements can usually be supplied either by way of the soil and plant or as mineral supplements to the common salt. This is particularly true of the ruminants.

The carnivores obtain mineral nutrients, including the common salt they require, by eating other animals. Man, partially a carnivore, may need extra common salt. And most of the other mineral elements he may require, over and above the quantities contained in his food, can be supplied in chemical salt forms. But there are two exceptions. Cobalt must be supplied as cobalamin or vitamin B^{12}. And the sulfur-containing amino acids, methionine, and possibly cystine, must be supplied in the form of some natural protein, such as meat, eggs, or milk, or in such plants as those of the cabbage family.

Plants grown in irrigated arid regions of the earth are usually rich in all the mineral nutrients required by man. In the United States, the mineral-nutrient, except for manganese, and protein values of plants tend to decrease from west to east, and carbohydrate values tend to increase. Turning southward, the carbohydrate content of plants tends to increase still further at the expense of mineral nutrients and proteins, and the quality of the proteins is lowered. Soils of high-rainfall areas are normally low in sulfur, and the plants growing on them tend to be low in the highly essential sulfur-containing amino acids, as well as in thiamine and biotin, two of the vitamin-B complex. This is particularly true of soils in the tropics; lack of industrial development in such areas means that relatively little sulfur will be contributed by way of the atmosphere and rain.

The several species of plants differ greatly in their contents and ratios of the mineral elements, even when growing on identical soils. These variations are related to differences in habits of growth, depth of root systems, rates of absorption by roots, and the heritages of the plants. In general, legumes are high in mineral elements and proteins. Sugar cane is an example of a semitropical plant that has low percentages of mineral elements and proteins and a high content of carbohydrate.

Certain species of plants tend to accumulate specific elements. Clover is an accumulator of cobalt; ragweed, of zinc; hickory, of aluminum; and beets, of sodium. Cabbage is an accumulator of sulfur; tobacco, of chlorine; and soybeans, of phosphorus. Sunflower is an accumulator of boron; locoweed (*Astragalus*), of selenium; devil's paint brush (*Hieracium*), of molybdenum; and horsetail (*Equisetum*), of silicon. Pigweed (*Amaranthus*) tends to accumulate nitrate.

Mineral deficiencies are likely to be much more widespread in animals than in man, because most animals are largely confined to a given farm where they consume the produce of just one general kind of soil. In contrast, modern man may consume the produce of many different kinds of soil, including those of the far corners of the world. The mineral nutrients that are missing in the produce of one soil may be supplied in large amounts in that of another soil. Toxic elements present in excess in the plants of one area may be almost entirely missing in those of another area. Thus the concentrations of all the mineral nutrients and of toxic elements may thus be averaged out to the point where neither deficiency nor toxicity develops.

Animals serve as testing agents for man in determining whether the produce of any given area can be consumed with safety, often losing their lives in the testing. Beef cattle and dairy cows serve as concentrators of the mineral nutrients and proteins required by man. This applies particularly to the trace elements, which tend to accumulate in the livers of animals, explaining the long-established practice of eating liver once a week. And the same principal applies to the consumption of salt-water fish, a common Friday article of diet.

Ruminants, of which sheep and cattle are our most important

examples, have considerable advantage nutritionally over man. In the rumens of these animals, feeds are processed microbially and then built back up into new nutritive units that normally meet all the requirements of animals. Those microbes can start with sugar, starch or cellulose, a chemical form of nitrogen like urea, and a mixed salt containing all the essential mineral nutrients and construct their own foods, which then become the food for the ruminant itself. An interesting development along this line is the use of liquid molasses, ethyl alcohol, phosphoric acid, urea, and mineral salts as a supplement to such crude, bulk feeds as corncobs, corn stalks, straw, and grass hays as a feed for beef cattle. By this means all of their requirements can be met at relatively low cost.

Meeting the food needs of man is a much more difficult problem. Not much synthesis of essential food units can be expected from the microbial population in his intestinal tract, although this is not to be entirely ruled out. For the most part, man must eat what he needs in the form of already synthesized organic substances in such products as grains, fruits, and vegetables, supplemented by milk, meat, eggs, and fish. The problem is one of selecting a balanced diet of carbohydrates, oils or fats, amino acids, and vitamins.

But the matter of mineral-nutrient balance must be dealt with. The tendency has been to consider that common salt, and the iodine that is generally added to it, meet all the supplemental-mineral requirements. The appetite of most people for common salt has been developed to the point where much more is consumed than is required. This has the effect of reducing the availability to the human system of the potassium, calcium, and magnesium in the foods eaten and that of the phosphorus as well. It would seem that foods should be chosen for their mineral-nutrient values, more or less in opposition to common salt.

Although man has the possibility of a wide and adequate nutritional base for meeting both his mineral and his organic food needs, he is not always able to take full advantage of this. Most of his food may come from a region that is covered with the same general kind of soil. Thus the Californians, for example, may consume mostly the products of the irrigated alkaline desert soils of that state. People of the corn belt are largely products of the surrounding neutral prairie soils. Much of the food eaten by New Englanders is grown on the low-lime acid soils of that region. The people of the South tend to consume a diet that is higher in carbohydrates and lower in proteins and minerals than that consumed in the central and western states. And the people of the tropics have still more carbohydrates and still fewer proteins and minerals in their diet.

Every man has a chemistry peculiar to himself. This applies to the size and shape of his vital organs, to his digestive processes, to his excretory pattern, and to his nutritional needs. Much of the malfunctioning of the bodies and minds of men in physical and mental distress can be accounted for in some abnormality of their chemistry. Some highly effective chemical remedies, including vitamins, mineral salts, and hormones, have effected cures of what were formerly believed to be incurable maladies in man. Nevertheless, there is an average nutritional need around which all the indispensable units of the diet, including the mineral nutrients—whether from the soil or from a mixed mineral salt—can be organized for the general welfare of the people as a whole.

Any troubles with mineral and amino-acid deficiencies in man arising from inadequate supplies or imbalances in the mineral nutrients in the soil of the area from which most of his food is obtained can readily be remedied. This calls for careful selection from among the foods grown within his area, supplemental purchases of foods from other areas, and consideration of needs for supplemental minerals as a part of the salt consumed. Most of the nutritional disorders of man are related to poor choice from among the many foods, both those of plant and animal origin. In some of the more densely populated parts of the world, however, the range in choice is often entirely too limited to meet requirements.

Infancy is a highly important period in the development of the human body. This applies particularly to that part of infancy that occurs before the child is born; the mother needs to have an adequate and well-balanced diet of minerals, proteins, and vitamins, as well as the necessary carbohydrates and fats. This continues to apply to the child after he is born, and particularly up to the time when he can be expected to exercise some intelligence of his own in the choice of foods. Children are often permitted to consume too-large amounts of high-carbohydrate candies, cookies, ice creams, and soft drinks at the expense of high-mineral and high-protein foods. And people in old age tend to eat too much of the foods and drinks that are easy to come by, such as bread and cakes and coffee and tea.

There is safety against mineral and protein deficiencies in the drinking of milk and the eating of edible products of animals. And, in a country like the United States, an animal economy is essential to the agricultural well-being of the nation. It provides a means of regulating food-crop surpluses, consumption of animal products going up and down in relation to the supplies of grain available for animal feeds.

Where food is scarce, as in the densely populated parts of the world, there is no economy in feeding grains to livestock and then consuming the meat and milk. At least 80 per cent of the energy value of grains is lost by feeding them to dairy cows and over 90 per cent by feeding them to beef cattle, and the efficiency of transforming plant proteins into animal proteins is only a little greater than this.

In proportion as people find it necessary to eat grains and other edible plant products as such, rather than in the form of animal products, extra precautions must be taken to see that the mineral, amino-acid, and vitamin values measure up to the requirements. This problem is a particularly difficult one to solve in the densely populated parts of the tropics. The lethargy common to the people of such regions may be due largely to deficiencies of this type, and this, even though they are living in the midst of many possibilities for abundant production of foods of the quality required.

De Castro says: "The so-called inferior races turn out to be starved races. Properly nourished they are in all respects equal to the would-be superior races. . . . Not only by acting on his body—degrading him in size, withering his flesh, gnawing at his viscera, and opening wounds in his skin—does hunger destroy the human being. It also acts on his spirit, on his mental structure, and on his social conduct." De Castro applies the term "human ponies" to the Asian peoples, saying that their height and weight have been lowered by chronic malnutrition. When these smaller races are fed mineral- and protein-rich meat, eggs, and milk, they soon grow in size and weight.

The agricultural lime and fertilizer industries have come to man's aid in this connection, providing a means by which the nitrogen and mineral supplies of soils can be replenished. And if such soil amendments are so formulated as to supply, by way of the soil, all the needs of the better types of crop plants, the amino-acid and most of the mineral and vitamin requirements of man can be met. This applies to the tropics as well as to the temperate zones.

Fortunately, the body of man has considerable capacity to hold on to the mineral nutrients in deficiency and to excrete those supplied in excess. What are known as "homeostatic mechanisms" protect him, in part, against the poverty of the soil on which his food was grown and against his own errors in the choice of foods. But man is subject to a lot of ills along the way that might well be warded off by paying more attention to his choice of foods and by assistance from those producing the foods he eats.

One cannot help but wonder about people who have lived much longer lives than those normally allotted to man. Thousands of people are known to have lived to be more than 100 years old. A few hardy souls have survived well into the second century. Bogomoletz, who spent a lifetime studying old age in man, tells of two old Russians who lived together to be 185. One old gentleman and his wife were said to have "dwelt together in connubial bliss for 147 years," dying at the ages of 172 and 164, respectively.

Christian Drakenburg is one of the famous old men of history. He was born in Denmark, spent most of his life as a romantic sailor, and died in 1772 at the age of 146. The most widely known of the world's old men is Thomas Parr whose body was buried beneath the floor of Westminster Abbey on November 15, 1635. The stone slab covering his grave records that he lived through the reigns of ten princes and died at the age of 152.

How did it happen that these men lived so long? Or, if these cases cannot be fully authenticated, what about the many other people who are known to have lived well beyond the century mark? Was this longevity due to the nature of the soil on which they got their start and from which their foods came? Was it due to fortunate choices in the foods they ate? Did they have especially good digestive and assimilative systems? Did they have some inborn resistance to disease? Or does the explanation lie in the old-ages genes in their ancestry?

Among the most illuminating studies of man in relation to his diet is that reported by Price. He traveled extensively among primitive peoples in widely distributed parts of the earth. His interest lay primarily in their teeth and in the formation of their jaws in relation to the food that was eaten. The one outstanding fact that developed in these studies was the disastrous effects that resulted when factory-processed foods were substituted too extensively for the cruder types of plant and animal products naturally available in their home communities.

One cannot help but wonder about Nebuchadnezzar. "He was driven from men and did eat grass as oxen, and his body was wet with the dew of heaven, 'til his hairs were grown like eagles' feathers and his nails like birds' claws."

The moldboard plow has been shown to be the villain of the world's agricultural drama.

—EDWARD H. FAULKNER IN *Plowman's Folly*

Chapter Twelve

THE MAN WITH THE PLOW

WHEN the first European settlers arrived in America, the larger part of what is now the forty-eight mainland states of the United States of America was covered with a dense growth of trees and grass. The roots of these perennial plants sewed the soil to Earth as firmly as any needle and thread ever attached a patch to the seat of a boy's pants.

Here and there open spaces among the trees had been taken over by the Indians and planted in corn and other food crops. Other areas of forest land had been burned over to bring in the grass and entice the deer. But most of the forest land had been left to nature. Giant trees grew up, died, and fell back on the soil. Farther west, where some 60 million buffaloes roamed the grazing lands at their disposal, much of the grass did likewise.

Over this vast expanse of forest and grassland, plants grew naturally, unmolested except by wild animals and some 800,000 Indians. The Indians may have lacked some of the facilities and aids to modern living, but they had what might be considered a much more important possession—the 2,400 acres of space that was available for every man, woman, and child.

Of necessity, our European ancestors began cutting down the giant forest trees along the eastern seaboard and putting the land to the plow. As the pioneer population grew and the people moved gradually westward against the Indians, they finally reached the prairies and plains where trees no longer posed a problem. But plowing the stiff prairie sod presented an even greater challenge, for the prairie grasses had developed a mass of roots such as few pioneers had ever experienced in their native lands. Nevertheless, they succeeded in breaking up the virgin sod and putting the land to work growing the crops of their choosing. In due time many millions of acres of this new land were being plowed each year and planted to a great variety of grain, legume, fiber, and vegetable crops.

Once the roots of the trees and grass that sewed the soil to Earth were broken and the land was laid bare, water and wind began to do their dirty work. At first the erosion of the soil was a slow process, scarcely noticeable to the man of the land. But when the rich supplies of organic matter that had accumulated in the forests and grasslands over the centuries had been plowed under and largely destroyed by microbes, which were stimulated to greater activity by cultivation operations, the soil became more subject to attack by the atmospheric elements. The steeper the slopes and the greater the rainfall, as in the East and South, the more rapid the loss of soil by water erosion. The drier the area and the higher the velocity of the winds, as on the Great Plains, the greater the damage done by dust storms.

The crops that the Indians had long grown soon became highly popular with the pioneers. These included corn, potatoes, tobacco, yams, snap beans, and tomatoes, all native to the Americas. Even the cotton, which soon came to be the dominant crop in the South, was new to the pioneers, although European armies had seen this crop when they invaded Egypt and the Near East.

The peculiarity about all these crops was that the land on which they were to be grown was not only plowed and worked in preparation for them, but the crops were planted in widely spaced rows, with cultivation between the rows during the early part of the growing season. Farmers soon began to take great pleasure in planting large fields of these new crops in long straight rows, no matter where the rows led. They took special pride in the straightness of the furrows that were made by the moldboard plows in preparation for planting. And the straight plant rows went up and down hill instead of across the slope as well. With each successive heavy rain larger amounts of topsoil flowed down the slopes, along the drainage channels, into the rivers, and out to sea.

It was not long until gullies began to form. Small at first, they began to enlarge, growing ever longer, deeper, and wider until machinery could no longer be pulled across them. More and more of the land had to be farmed in smaller fields that often became mere patches, with deep gullies in between.

Even where the land was relatively level, heavy downpours began carrying away large amounts of soil by sheet erosion. This was readily apparent after each heavy rainstorm when small pebbles were left standing on slim pedestals of soil that had been protected by them against the eroding action of the raindrops. But few farmers appeared to notice what was happening in these level fields, although the muddy water that flowed across the land and down the streams must certainly have caused them some concern.

Unfortunately, the climate of the United States is one of extremes in rainfall, temperature, wind, and drouth. The total annual rainfall—including the snow, which is calculated to rain—in the region east of the Mississippi averages between thirty-five and sixty inches or more a year from area to area. Westward the rainfall drops to thirty, twenty-five, twenty, and fifteen inches a year, and then becomes still lower toward the Great American Desert, where it is virtually nil. But whether the rainfall is high or low, it tends to come in heavy downpours, often with high winds. And drouths of varying lengths, from weeks and months to years, occur between these heavy rains.

Our European ancestors had not been accustomed to farming under conditions of storms, floods, high winds, and drouths. The rainfall of the British Isles and central Europe, from which they mostly came, is one of gentle showers that do relatively little damage to the soil, particularly under the cropping systems that are largely being employed. The rainfall around London, Paris, and Berlin is about twenty-five inches a year. It comes so gently and is so well-distributed over the season that it is comparable in crop effect to that of our New England States, where the temperatures are much the same but the rainfall, in larger doses, is from forty to forty-five inches annually. The twenty-five-inch annual rainfall area in the United States, extending from the central part of the Dakotas southward across western Oklahoma and Texas to the Río Grande Valley, is a relatively drouthy area, the center of the dust bowl.

It took quite a long while for the early settlers and their descendants to realize the serious toll the rain and wind were taking on the soil that was being plowed and planted to these new American clean-cultivated wide-rowed crops. This was due in large part to the abundance of new land to be had farther west when the productivity and farmability of the older land in the eastern part of the country had dropped well below what it had been originally.

But those who remained to continue farming this older land gradually became aware that a lot of good topsoil, and much of the manure, lime, and fertilizer that were being applied to it, was being carried away by the rain. Unproductive subsoil was coming to the surface to take its place. In many cases land so eroded had to be abandoned. When this happened, weeds took over, and the weeds were gradually replaced by grass, briars, shrubs, and trees, in fairly rapid succession. This was nature's way of healing the wounds inflicted by man, reclaiming the bare land, and gradually renewing its productive capacity.

Ultimately, the trees grew into usable timber, which again became a primary source of income. In Virginia and other states of the South the corn rows of old plantations can often be found running straight through second-growth forests. Once this new growth of timber is harvested, some of the land is again being returned to farming, but under improved methods of erosion control.

In the drier regions of the Great Plains, sod that never should have been broken was put to the plow in preparation for wheat production, particularly during the necessary expansion required by World War I. This wheat land, when later abandoned because of widespread drouth, low productivity, and low grain prices, was difficult to deal with. The rainfall was usually insufficient to permit quick establishment of a new grass cover between drouths. As a result, large acreages of this land became subject to troublesome dust storms that picked up large tonnages of soil and carried it eastward across the country.

Such dust storms have been repeated over much of this region after each successive drouth. Severe drouths have occurred about every thirty-five years, with lesser ones in between.

Trouble with blowing sand and soil will continue until such time as virtually the entire area is again covered with sod and overgrazing with beef cattle and sheep is brought under control. In the Mediterranean countries and the Near East, goats have added greatly to the problems involved in dealing with semiarid lands. Trees, shrubs, weeds, and grass are eaten down to the ground, and little vegetation remains to protect the soil. It might be well to remember that Mohair goats have gotten well-established in southwest Texas, with another half-million scattered about over other parts of the southwest. In time of drouth, they leave nothing but the thorns of the broad-leaved cactus and the stripped branches of the mesquite trees.

Loss of topsoil, whether by wind or water, is bad for the land, bad for the people who live on it, bad for the nearby towns and cities, bad for the states in which it occurs, and bad for the nation as a whole. One of the most troublesome off-the-land problems that arises in this connection is the damage that results to downstream reservoirs of impounded water being stored for city use or for irrigation purposes. Many such reservoirs are being rapidly filled with soil, the average rate of loss of storage capacity being from 2 to 3 per cent a year. Lake Mead, behind the highly expensive Hoover Dam on the Colorado River, is being filled with silt, its life being estimated at less than 150 years.

Experience with these problems has led to the conclusion that no such impoundments of water should be attempted until adequate conservation measures have been applied to the land in the watersheds that drain into them. This calls for a variety of measures of which some will apply to one area and others to another. But enough is now known about the solution of these problems that dependable recommendations can be made by those employed in such work.

Tremendous tonnages of good soil go downstream during every flood. And no matter how well-laid the plans to bring floods under control, an occasional one gets beyond bounds, doing tremendous damage. In 1950, for example, the floods associated with hurricane Diane caused an estimated 1,675 million dollars of damage to land and property in southern New England. The United States as a whole has to deal with an average daily runoff of 1,250 billion gallons of water, with large ups and downs in flow from time to time and place to place.

Much of the soil that is carried downstream is spread out on top of other good soil in the flooded areas. But large quantities are carried farther downstream to form troublesome deposits in river beds at the points where they empty into larger rivers or into the gulfs and bays. Heavy expenditures are required annually to free river channels of such deposits so that vessels can continue to navigate them.

Something similar to what happened to the soil of the United States was also happening to its forests and wildlife. Consequently, a number of groups of people, representing various interests, were organized to deal with the many problems involved. Over forty regional and national associations of this type are now joined into the National Resources Council of America, with headquarters in Washington, D. C.

Conservation, as viewed by the groups represented by this council, has to do with the preservation for improved use of all our renewable natural resources, including not only soil and water but forests, grasslands, field crops, livestock, wildlife, fish, and recreational areas. All these resources are capable of being made available in ever greater abundance in perpetuity. In this respect they differ fundamentally from the nonrenewable coal, petroleum, natural gas, and ore resources.

The primary purpose of the several groups of conservationists is to devise ways and means by which waste of the renewable natural resources they represent can be reduced to a minimum. Having done this, the next task is that of getting conservation measures into full operation on the land, requiring a long and continuous educational program that can become fully effective only with time. It also requires permissive, remedial, and preventive legislation, both state and national, with some regulatory provisions.

Two agencies of the United States Department of Agriculture, the Soil Conservation Service and the Forest Service, are specifically designed for the purpose of conserving renewable natural resources. The Fish and Wildlife Service and the National Park Service of the federal Department of the Interior are two other highly important conservation agencies. All of these agencies have their main offices in Washington, D. C., but most of the personnel employed work out in the open country where the renewable natural resources are located. And co-operating conservation agencies are found in every one of the forty-eight mainland states and in Alaska and Hawaii.

The starting point in any national or state program for conserving renewable natural resources is the soil. Unless the soil can be kept where it is or where it has been deliberately placed by man, unless it is protected against loss by wind and water erosion, and unless it is maintained in a high state of productivity, conservation of other renewable natural resources cannot be satisfactorily effected. The first need in dealing with the soil on a state and national basis is for a careful survey of the entire area of land in relation to its capabilities for use. This involves mapping the soil on the basis of its physical, chemical, and biological properties, its depth and drainage, and the lay of the land on which it lies.

Well-trained soil scientists of the Soil Conservation Service, assigned to assess the capabilities of the entire land area of the United States, decided that it could be conveniently divided into eight soil-capability classes. Classes I, II, III, and IV include all the land that is suitable for crop-production purposes when proper consideration is given to soil and water conservation measures. These classes are based primarily on topography, depth of soil, and water relationships. In general, the topography of these four classes of land is level, gently rolling, moderately sloping, and strongly sloping, respectively.

Class V land includes that of limited agricultural usefulness because of such unfavorable factors as stoniness, shallowness, dryness, or wetness. Classes VI, VII, and VIII lands include, in general, that located on steep, very steep, and mountainous topography, respectively. Most of the land in these last three classes is suitable only for grazing, forestry, wildlife, or mining. Some of it is essentially waste, with little chance of its being brought into use for any purpose except recreation in the foreseeable future.

Land-use maps, colored in conformity with the several classes of soil and their conservation needs, are now being provided for those concerned in one manner or another with specific pieces of land. Green areas on such maps indicate land that can be used for cropping purposes with little likelihood of serious loss of soil by erosion, assuming it is reasonably well-managed. Yellow areas include land on which caution must be employed. Red is used for land that is subject to serious losses of soil by wind and water erosion under cultivation operations and on which specific precautionary measures must be taken. And purple indicates land that should be devoted primarily to grass and forests, with possibly occasional use for growing small grains and cultivated crops under suitable controls.

Thousands of farmers have come to realize the necessity of adopting strict conservation measures to control wind and water and to save the soil. A great deal of steep land has been taken out of crop production and put into permanent grass or trees. Large areas of what was once wheat land in the drier parts of the Great Plains have been successfully reseeded to permanent grass for controlled grazing by beef cattle and sheep.

Most of the more erodible cropped land is now being farmed in conformity with one or more of the well-established conservation practices. The most common of these are contouring, terracing, stubble-mulching, and cover cropping under a crop rotation program. Excess water is carried off the land in grassed waterways. High winds are controlled by planting windbreaks, which may either be such temporary types as rye, planted for harvesting, or the more permanent shrubs or tress.

Contour farming requires preparing the land and planting the crops around the slopes rather than up and down them. Terracing involves the building of ridges of soil slightly off the contour to carry excess water away slowly to be emptied into grassed waterways. Stubble-mulching calls for leaving crop refuse on top the surface of the soil and having the crop plants come up through it. Cover cropping is the growing of a close-rowed crop like rye to protect the land between the growing of cultivated crops, this rye being plowed under while still green. And crop rotation is the growing of wide-rowed, close-rowed, and grass-clover crops in succession as aids to reducing loss of soil and water.

In contour farming a series of levels are run by the use of a land surveying instrument. In highly intensive farming areas, land leveling and actual excavation and movement of large volumes of soil may be resorted to for the purpose of getting the contour areas or strips into more readily farmable units. Not only the plowing in preparation for planting but all the other farm operations are carried on along the contour lines.

The best means of preventing soil erosion, whether by wind or water, is to keep the land permanently covered with close-growing plants, such as grasses and forest trees. The tops of these plants break the fall of raindrops, the water flowing down their stems to the soil. But there is a great need for millions of acres of corn, potatoes, cotton, and such other wide-rowed cultivated crops as tomatoes and vegetables. As a rule, these crops come into maturity in the fall, and special precautions must be taken to get the land covered with some close-growing crop, such as wheat, rye, or some winter legume, of which vetch in the North and crimson clover in the South are excellent examples. Failing this, the hope lies in having a sufficient quantity of crop wastes, such as straw, corn stalks, or other refuse left on the land to protect it against atmospheric factors.

A great deal of attention is being given to developing improved means of making better use of crop wastes as a means of protecting the soil. These are left lying on top the land during the winter, as with corn stalks, or they are partly worked into the soil, as with wheat straw, in preparation for reseeding. Back of these practices is the idea of doing away with the moldboard plow, which turns a furrow, buries the sod or other crop refuse in the bottom, and leaves nothing but clean soil exposed on the surface. To leave the trash on top, use can be made of the small-disk type cultivators or the tool-bar cultivators which consist of narrow blades that extend down into the soil for the purpose of breaking it up. The duckfoot cultivator, which carries wide blades that spread out horizontally and are pulled through the soil three or four inches below the surface is widely used in Nebraska and nearby states.

The trash system works best in the drier parts of the country and on the sandier soils. It is widely used on the corn and wheat lands in Kansas and other states in that area and on the cotton and soybean lands on the coastal plains of the Carolinas. It is not so satisfactory in the northeastern quarter of the United States, where the trash delays the drying-out of the soil in the spring and interferes with the planting of crops.

On the steeper slopes strip cropping is an excellent procedure. This calls for growing alternate strips of a wide-rowed cultivated crop like corn, a closer-rowed uncultivated crop like wheat, and a sod crop like grass and clover, all planted on the contour. On looking at the side of such a slope one sees long, relatively narrow strips of various colors, each a different crop. Where the cultivated crop is this year, the small-grain crop will be next year and the grass-clover crop the third year. When plowing the land on such slopes, the furrow is generally thrown uphill. In central Europe any soil that accumulates at the bottom of such a slope during the summer is often hauled back up to the top of the slope later in the year.

The saving of soil and water is the starting point and the most important step in conservation of the renewable natural resources of the nation. This applies whether one is thinking of the land itself, the plants that are growing on it, or the living things that depend on the produce of the land. It applies whether the end point of the effort is livestock, wildlife, fish, or man.

But many wasteful practices other than those relating to needless loss of soil and unnecessary runoff of water must be brought under control. The native grasses of America, the native wildlife on which the Indians placed much of their dependence for food, and the native forests that grew in such abundance in the humid parts of the continent merit much more study toward improvement by selection and breeding. And although outside the scope of this book, a great deal more attention needs to be given to the prevention of needless waste of nonrenewable natural resources. This is particularly important in connection with the conservation of our phosphate rock deposits. The late Richard Van Hise, former president of the University of Wisconsin, a geologist and pioneer in conservation, considered these deposits to be the most important of all our nonrenewable natural resources and the ones in greatest need of conservation. The reason for his particular concern with the phosphate rock deposits lay in their importance for replacing the phosphorus that is lost from the soil in drainage waters and harvested crops, its final repository being either the buried bones of man or the bottom of the sea.

One of the most important happenings in soil and water conservation in the United States was the development of the concept of organizing the country into soil conservation districts operating under state control. Such districts offer real opportunity for community effort and accomplishment. Some three thousand of them now cover the major part of the nation's land resources, each being governed by a board of from three to five farmers who have been selected by their neighbors for their capacity for constructive leadership. These men are in position to render highly important services to their districts, and many of them do.

A soil conservation district may be a small valley, a large watershed, a county, or several counties joined together. The district supervisors promote conservation practices among their neighbors by setting good examples. They bring the people together from time to time to consider the larger aspects of the district's problems that cannot be dealt with individually. They enlist the aid of technicians of the Soil Conservation Service and of those of all the other federal, state, county and local agencies that can lend a hand in getting conservation on the land. They endeavor to govern their districts by persuasion rather than compulsion.

Sometimes group interest may be primarily in contour farming or strip cropping or in terracing the land. It may be in developing sodded waterways or in the construction of ponds or larger reservoirs. It may be in building flood prevention dams in the upper reaches of their watershed, or in flood control dams downstream. It may be in drainage, land leveling, or pasture improvement.

Often great interest is found in planting trees, protecting wildlife, and improving fishing facilities. Frequently community interest is built around the general beautification of a valley and the preservation of the purity of the water in the stream that flows through it. Whatever this beginning interest may be, it provides a starting point out of which an over-all conservation program can be developed.

Often progress is very slow, but sometimes it is rapid indeed. A National Association of Soil Conservation Districts is now taking an aggressive interest in furthering conservation by way of the several districts. It is endeavoring to aid them in getting more federal technical service and larger federal appropriations with which to operate more effectively. It has set down some other long-time goals toward which it strives. These include obtaining larger state appropriations for soil conservation districts, inaugurating more upstream watershed control, making the districts co-ordinating bodies for all soil and water conservation effort, giving their programs priority in credit and technical assistance, and seeing that all funds allotted for soil and water conservation are so used.

Probably no other nation has developed a more forward-looking program for conserving its renewable natural resources than the United States of America. Vast areas exist in various parts of the world where little or nothing has ever been done toward bringing the forces of nature under control in relation to agricultural practice. This applies particularly to many parts of Mexico, Central America, South America, and the mainland of China.

Much of the devastation of the land in the countries bordering on the Mediterranean Sea and extending into the interior of Asia Minor can be explained by the wars that have raged through this region. But the fundamental cause of the poverty of the agriculture of this region lies in the destruction of the forests, the cultivation of steep lands, the overgrazing of pasturelands by sheep and goats, and the resulting erosion of the soil that was permitted to occur. The soil from the hill lands was eroded down into the valleys where it covered up good soil in humid regions and filled the canals with sediment in the irrigated arid areas.

Under such circumstances the farmers have remained poverty-stricken peasants. They have neither the understanding of the problem nor the necessary funds with which to undertake the very costly conservation measures that are needed to bring the badly eroded land back to its original state of productivity as a starting point for the further improvements required to support the ever growing populations.

Some of the best examples of conservation of renewable natural resources are found in central and western Europe. There the land is relatively level, rainfall comes in frequent light showers, and the possibilities of wind and water erosion are much less than they are in many other parts of the world. But a primary reason for the excellent state of conservation of these European lands is found in the love of the people for the soil on which they live and the intelligence that is applied to its use in food and forest production. The relatively dense populations and high living standards of these countries do not permit waste of renewable natural resources. Grass and trees are systematically grown and harvested on the steeper land that is not suitable for crop production. Where crops are grown, the land is so carefully husbanded that very little of the soil is left bare.

Returning to the United States, the most promising feature of the conservation movement is that the men who are employed in developing and bringing into operation the best procedures on the land are dedicated to their task. They are missionaries who are so firmly convinced of the importance of their work that they find compensations far beyond that of the salaries or wages they are paid.

Hugh H. Bennett, of North Carolina, more than any other man, was responsible for getting soil and water conservation recognized as a specific part of the activities of the federal Department of Agriculture. As a soil-survey specialist of that department, Bennett had had abundant opportunity to study the soil at first hand. He was worried about what he saw. Everywhere he went the handwriting of erosion was apparent in the ever deepening gullies and the ever larger areas of subsoil that had come to the surface. The streams of the South ran red with soil after every rain. He expanded his studies to include the entire South, Cuba, Puerto Rico, and, eventually, South America, the Near East, and southeast Asia as well.

Bennett was particularly disturbed by land that was allowed to lie bare during the winter months after a crop like corn or cotton had been harvested from it. The heavy rains beat directly on the soil in these bare fields, loosening the clay particles and carrying them off the fields in quantity. Under his leadership a great variety of methods were developed for protecting the land in the interim between one crop and the next. Cover crops were planted late in the season so that when rain fell it would strike the leaves of these plants and flow slowly down the stems instead of striking the soil directly. Much more attention was given to seeding the rougher land to permanent grass and to planting forest trees in those areas where crop production was not advisable.

Out of Bennett's efforts a permanent Soil Conservation Service was firmly established with the passage of the Soil Conservation Act of 1935. This act is probably the most important piece of national legislation with respect to the conservation of land resources the world has ever known. The aim of the Soil Conservation Service, and of all the other conservation agencies, is not only to stop soil erosion, to control floods, to protect wildlife, to improve forests, and to beautify the country, but to develop a high sense of appreciation of responsibility for the soil and for all our other renewable natural resources. The hope is that when the young people of today have become the leaders of thought and action tomorrow, they will do a still better job of conserving these resources than their fathers have done.

Nature paints the best part of the picture, carves the best part of the statue, builds the best part of the house, and speaks the best part of the oration.

—RALPH WALDO EMERSON

Chapter Thirteen

THE COUNTRY BEAUTIFUL

DID you ever stand beneath the boughs of a mighty oak, a tall pine, or a thousand-year-old sequoia tree in a virgin forest far removed from the haunts of man? Did you ever drive leisurely across a wide expanse of unplowed prairies or plain with a team of horses attached to your wagon? If so, you can visualize at least in part what a magnificent and spacious Indian paradise this land of ours must once have been.

This is still a magnificent country, even though in their haste to conquer it our forefathers did a considerable amount of almost irreparable damage to some of our renewable natural resources and even though they were often careless in the exploitation of the non renewable types. In a relatively short period of time the settlers of this fabulously rich country cut down millions of forest trees and plowed up millions of acres of grass, with much unnecessary waste of timber, sod, and soil and with little thought of their conservation for continued use.

But there are compensations. Large areas of land that were once covered with forest and grass are now being devoted to the production of crops of equally attractive appearance and certainly of much greater usefulness to the more than 180 million people who now live on the mainland of the United States of America. The many millions of acres of well-tended corn and soybeans of the central states, of cotton and peanuts in the South, and of wheat and oats to the west and elsewhere have as great an eye appeal and certainly much higher food value than the native forests and grasslands they replaced.

It is difficult to imagine anything more rewarding to the eye of the country-minded man than grains, tobacco, sugar beets, potatoes, and vegetables when grown to a high state of productivity by the farmers who know how to do it. The large fields of ladino, red, alsike, white, and crimson clovers that abound in full bloom in their season are there for everyone to enjoy. The wide expanses of alfalfa, with their purple blossoms, and the somewhat smaller acreages of sweet clover, with their more noticeable white and yellow blossoms, attract the eye. And a few of nature's original offerings compare with the many acres of apple and cherry orchards of the North, with their pink blossoms and dark red fruits, or the citrus groves of the South, with their dark-green foliage and golden yellow oranges.

Much of the exploitation of our natural resources was necessary in meeting the ever enlarging needs of a rapidly growing population. But a large part of the damage that was done to the virgin beauty of the landscape, to the land itself, and to the wildlife that abounded could readily have been avoided if adequate plans for their conservation could first have been developed and put into operation. It is quite surprising that such disastrous disturbances to nature could have occurred at the hands of the conservation-minded European pioneers who came from countries where land was cherished and people were painfully aware of the great importance of keeping the soil in a high state of productivity and the forest in good repair.

The United States is a young country, its first permanent English settlement having been established at Jamestown, Virginia, in 1607. Its vast land area was overrun in a hurry, and habits of waste and extravagance soon were developed because of the wealth of natural resources at the pioneers' disposal. Much is now being done to arouse public interest in the necessity for conserving our renewable natural resources in keeping with the ever greater demands that are being made on them, and many people are highly responsive to such appeals. Yet there is great need to develop much wider recognition of our obligation to keep this a permanently beautiful as well as productive country. And there is still greater need for specific suggestions how this can best be accomplished.

Cutting down the original forest trees and breaking up the native grass sods were not necessarily crimes against nature. Everything depended on the purposes for which these actions were being done and the care that was exercised in doing them. And, given an opportunity, nature is capable of repairing much of the damage. Unless the land is to be used for factory, business, housing, or highway purposes, trees, grass, and other equally useful and beautiful vegetation can be made to grow again. And much can be done even with the grounds around industrial plants to make them more attractive to the passers-by and more satisfying to those who work there.

The better-watered regions of the United States were originally covered with such deciduous trees as oak, hickory, maple, elm, sycamore, and poplar, or with such evergreens as pine, hemlock, spruce, and fir. On the more rolling to mountainous lands the descendants of these original trees still abound and are being permitted to reseed themselves. But much more care is now being used in the maintenance of tree stands. Forest fires, such as the one that destroyed forty thousand acres of timber near San Diego, California, in 1956, are being more quickly brought under control, or entirely prevented. And more and more of the native trees are being systematically replaced with improved species, as well as being managed under controlled harvesting procedures.

Once the forests of the humid regions were cut down and the sods of the prairies and plains were turned with the plow, the soil was exposed to the elements as it had never been before. This being a country of violent windstorms and heavy downpours of rain, the United States soon had many badly eroded hillsides, great gullies across once level fields, moving sands along the shores of lakes and seas, and disastrous dust storms in the dry interior. Some of the by-products of such erosive action were ugliness of the landscape, impoverished people, and country slums.

The problems involved in conserving all the land that must be plowed and planted in food and fiber crops are quite complex in comparison with those involved in protecting forest lands and adding to them. Forest trees, like grass, automatically protect the soil against erosion by water and wind. But in growing field corps farmers are faced with the necessity of protecting bare soil against these erosive forces. Once the close-rowed small grains or the closely seeded grasses and legumes get established, their root systems hold the soil in place. Yet the problem persists until such time as this has been effected, and it continues throughout the growing season for crops like corn and cotton that are planted in rows several feet apart with cultivation in between.

The starting point in the conservation of natural beauty is the soil itself. Bare soil is a blot on the landscape. Given an opportunity, nature hastens to cover its bareness, first with weeds, then with grass and shrubs, and, under conditions of adequate moisture, with tall trees. But in semiarid and arid regions, or where the fertile topsoil has been eroded off the land and subsoil is now on the surface, the rate of renewal of the vegetative cover may be extremely slow. And if wind and water are permitted to carry on their erosive actions, it may not be possible to develop a new cover without man's assistance.

Yet there are much larger and more disturbing aspects to the problem than these. People are greatly influenced by their surroundings. If they are careless about the land on which they live they tend to become even more careless about themselves. Ignorance, immorality, and crime tend to grow and thrive in areas where the natural beauty of the surroundings has been destroyed; this applies to country and city alike. When attention is given to correcting such conditions, the people living in these areas and participating in their renovation tend to take on greatly improved attitudes as well.

Under the very bad conditions that were permitted to develop on the land in many parts of this country following the exploitation of the renewable natural resources without regard to the employment of preventive and restorative measures, nature herself was impoverished. In many areas the rich topsoil largely disappeared, the subsoil came to the surface, the supplies of nitrogen and readily available mineral nutrients were exhausted, and the soil became inhospitable to plants. The natural recovery processes were then too slow to meet requirements.

Where such conditions have prevailed it becomes necessary to do something constructive to speed up vegetative growth and get the bare land covered as quickly as possible. Applications of manures, liming materials, and fertilizers help, but the impoverished farmer on the land may not be able to provide them. Fortunately, some of the legumes, which are able to collect the nitrogen they need from the atmosphere through the aid of the bacteria in the nodules on their roots, can often get under way on impoverished soils. Sweet clover, birdsfoot trefoil, and hairy vetch are such crops in the North, whereas lespedeza, kudzu, and lupines are able to grow and thrive on relatively poor soils in the South. Locust trees, also legumes, are equally useful for such purposes. Nursery-grown improved species of other trees can be planted to full stands in cut-over forest lands, instead of waiting for nature's slower and less dependable reseeding methods. Range lands can be seeded with improved strains of grasses that are more sturdy and have greater resistance to drouth, and if these grasses can be lightly fertilized and protected against overgrazing, they may soon be able to get under way to full stands.

One of the most constructive measures undertaken to date in an effort to protect soil against further erosion is that of mapping the land resources in accordance with their use-capabilities. Once such a map has been made of any given farm, the owner and operator have a dependable basis for deciding how much of the land can safely be put in harvested crops. And the map also gives them an indication of the precautions that must be taken in dealing with the soil in preparation for planting crops and in growing them to maturity. It further indicates the areas that can best be devoted to some type of permanent but still profitable cover, such as grass or trees.

Our present concepts of private ownership of land do not permit controlling destructive actions of an owner or operator.

If the owner wants to build a factory or develop a housing area on some of the best farming land, there is nothing to stop him, except for a relatively few agriculturally zoned areas. Over one million acres of good farm land are lost to agriculture every year in such developments in the various parts of the United States. If a farmer wants to plow and cultivate rough land that should be kept in grass or trees, that is his privilege. And the large acreages of badly eroded land the country over that now are essentially wasteland provide ample evidence of the lack of good judgment or the lack of concepts of obligation to posterity by owners and operators of such land.

The small-watershed approach to the solution of conservation problems has been found highly effective in many localities. It joins the interests of all the people in a watershed and enables them to see better what their individual conservation obligations are to the community in which they live. And, by joint efforts, improvements can be effected that would otherwise have been impossible. Uncontrolled rainwater in the upper part of a watershed may become uncontrollable flood water farther down the valley. With the development of co-operative effort and the improvements that come to pass, a certain pride develops in the community that gradually results not only in making it a better place in which to live but in having better people living there.

Although many owners are motivated in considerable degree by a spirit of altruism, there must generally be some economic reward for expenditures toward the conservation of renewable natural resources on the land. Such a reward is usually there, but too much time may be required for its fulfillment to make it attractive to, or even possible of realization by, the present owner or operator of the land. Even though improvement of the land for its own sake and in the interests of posterity has a certain appeal, that alone is insufficient to get it done on an adequate scale.

With change in management arising from the death of the owner or from sale of the land, the educational process often has to be started all over again. Thus conservation problems and preventive measures must be dealt with in perpetuity. The hope lies in the gradual development of a tradition of conservation of both beauty and productiveness that will be so well-grounded as not to permit further misuse of the land in a community.

Usually the people who remain in areas where widespread misuse of renewable natural resources has been permitted to occur are financially unable to undertake restorative measures, even if they are so inclined. Local, state, or federal purchases of such land for reforestation provide one answer in humid regions; much of this has been done, notably in the state of New York. Re-establishment of a good cover of improved grasses at public expense, followed by controlled grazing, is virtually the only remedy for the bad state of much of the land being returned to pasture in the dust bowl of the Great Plains.

The federal government, the several states, and many communities have undertaken large- and small-scale conservation programs of various kinds. The most comprehensive of such programs is that of the Tennessee Valley Authority, established in 1933, with its twenty-nine large dams for water control and power development. This project has had a rejuvenating effect on a large part of that state and on the hilly to mountainous areas in neighboring states. Texas has established the Brazos River Authority, with a six-dam program and the building of a chain of lakes 250 miles long. Ohio has similar authorities for flood control, starting with the one that began its undertakings immediately after the devastating flood in the Miami Valley in 1913, and followed by another in the Muskingum Valley at Zanesville a few years later. The Stony Brook project at Princeton, New Jersey, is an excellent example of what a local community can do to foster soil and water conservation. The aim of all these agencies is not only to control floods, stop soil erosion, improve agriculture, develop prosperous communities, protect wildlife, and beautify the countryside, but to develop a high sense of appreciation of and responsibility for the soil and the other renewable natural resources.

In all cases, means must be developed for getting as large a percentage as possible of the rain and snow to soak into the soil where it falls, rather than to let it run off the surface. A great many devices are being employed to accomplish this purpose and, where necessary, to protect the soil against the erosive action of any necessary runoff. These include the use of some kind of ground cover that protects the soil against the directly eroding action of the ralling raindrops. They also include such measures as contour farming, strip cropping, and diversion terracing. They may include storage dams by which water is held back in the upper reaches of the watershed both for flood prevention and for irrigation.

If a good cover of grass or trees could be established on all the land that now lies bare, or essentially so, for no very good reason, many of the present muddy streams would run clear during most of the year. Some of the advantages of this are readily apparent. But others, such as the fitness of the water for fish and for drinking by both wild and domestic animals, are often passed over without thought of the consequences. The appearance of the countryside and of the premises of factories, housing areas, and other installations where bare soil is permitted to exist could certainly be greatly improved, and quickly, to the advantage of all concerned.

Good appearances of both surroundings and buildings of industrial properties as well as of farming lands and homesteads is highly important in terms of the attitudes of the workmen associated with them. Once an employee has become accustomed to ugliness he tends to accept it without further thought, losing interest in doing anything to improve the situation. In fact, he is quite likely to reach a state of mind in which he is no longer aware of the existence of such conditions, passing by them daily without any concern whatsoever.

No matter how beautiful, well-kept, and productive forests, grasslands, and croplands may be or how satisfying the many well-cared-for gardens, lawns, and recreational parks, these alone may not suffice for meeting the needs of the man whose daily task takes him to an unattractive location. All men must live and work, but many of them find themselves spending day after day, month after month, and year after year in surroundings that are far removed from nature's touch. One is often impressed by the amount of loving care that is being given to a lonely potted plant in a window of some building located in drab surroundings.

The possibilities for ugliness are far greater in industrial centers than they are in the open country. And this ugliness may be particularly distressing to the man who was born out in the great open spaces and has a nature-educated eye and mind. Two questions arise. How can the lack of attractiveness of factories, business districts, and unsightly housing developments be overcome? And how can more of them be prevented from coming into being?

Here the trained eye and hand of the building and landscape architect come into play. Certainly such men are as much disturbed by what they often see being constructed out of wood, stone, glass, and metal or by what is being done with the grounds roundabout as the soil conservationist is by what he sees happening to much of the farming land. But neither the architect nor the conservationist can persuade all of his constituents to do all the things that should be done, in the way they should be done, and at the time they should be done.

Monstrosities of masonry are more likely to stand out as unsightly monuments to a lack of understanding of the city man than eroded hillsides and ragged forests are to a lack of appreciation of nature on the part of the land owner and farmer. Solid but ugly city structures may remain for centuries where they were erected. But, given a fair chance, nature has a way of overcoming the unsightliness of eroded and mistreated land out in the country. Even the weeds that spring up on bare spots are frequently attractive. Often various kinds of quite beautiful vines and shrubs quickly cover eroded areas so effectively that they disappear entirely from view. And grass or trees finally take over.

Artists are being employed to study the use of paint in special ways in overcoming the drab appearances of some of the oil refineries and other chemical plants. Many factories are now being established on spacious grounds some distance from the city, and particular attention is being paid to landscaping the surrounding grounds. Special efforts are made by some industries to develop housing areas for their employees in attractive locations, with well-planned recreational grounds nearby. Highway engineers are taking ever greater pains to make the rights of way more scenic to the motorist, space between the two directions of travel being widened and landscaped and curves and dips being developed to avoid the monotony of long distances of travel over straight roads across uninteresting flat lands.

But there are many places where the needed improvements are not being made. Included among the distressing sights along the highways are the automobile cemeteries, the rat-infested city dumps, the dilapidated burial grounds, and the great variety of unsightly signs and billboards that often litter the landscape along the rights of way. Many of the roadside advertising signs are not only ugly in themselves but interfere greatly with the passers-by's seeing the highly satisfying evidence of nature's handiwork. And many people are so unresponsive to neatness and cleanliness that they drop litter of every imaginable kind along the highways, on city streets, and in other public places. Many a farmer has granted permission to some group of picnickers to stop at a shady spot on his property, or they have stopped without his permission, only to find that they departed, leaving their refuse scattered about.

Fortunately, many excellent examples of the conservation of renewable natural resources for continued and improved use and examples of the beautification of home grounds and business properties have been set by people in various walks of life the world over. Many millions of acres of carefully planted, tended, fire-protected, and regularly harvested and replanted forest are found. This applies particularly to the more progressive parts of central and western Europe and more recently, in an ever increasing degree, to North America as well. Large acreages of what would otherwise be wasteland have been put into recreational and wildlife preserves. Even a small country like the Netherlands, with its high-density population, finds it possible to set aside considerable areas of attractively developed land for use in meeting the outdoor needs of its city people.

Yellowstone National Park is one of a great many excellent examples of such dedication of land to meeting the needs of nature-loving people in the United States of America. Large acreages of rough and wet land have been set aside in other areas as wildlife preserves. And spacious recreational spots are being developed the country over. The fact that these natural preserves of land, trees, grass, shrubbery, rivers, and lakes are being overrun with people during the summer months points impressively not only to the interest of these people in the beauty and spaciousness of nature but to their desire for recreational opportunities in the open country. It is highly important that these needs be recognized and that plans be developed on a larger scale for meeting them, before it is too late. Alaska has great present and much greater potential value in this connection.

Conservation is a way of life. It starts with man himself. It begins anew each day as he takes his morning bath, shaves, and puts on a clean shirt. It induces him to keep his trousers pressed and his shoes shined. It requires that he make himself presentable to his family and his fellow men. He aims to look and act his best. This is conservation of self respect.

If he owns a home, the conservation-minded man keeps it painted and in good repair. He strives for an attractive lawn that is free of weeds. He helps his wife in landscaping the premises and he encourages her with her flowers. He tries to put the idea of the orderliness and neatness of nature across to his children. No trash is permitted to accumulate about his property. Leaves and other plant refuse are made into compost or carted away. Paper and similar waste is picked up regularly and disposed of. Everything is kept neat and clean about the premises. This is conservation of home and family.

If this man is a farmer, he sees that something is made to grow wherever a bare spot appears in an uncultivated field. He will not permit development of gullies that grow ever larger on his farm. He endeavors to keep the water that flows through his land crystal clear as much of the time as possible. He plants his cultivated crops on the contour, carries off the surplus in sodded runways, and sows cover crops to protect his land during the winter months. Rough land is seeded down in grass or planted with trees. This is conservation of soil.

Such a man takes the necessary measures to insure that as much as possible of the rain water soaks into the soil where it falls. To this end, he leaves the crop refuse on top the land wherever feasible instead of plowing it under. He constructs a pond to store water for emergencies and to provide a recreation center for his family and friends. He participates in the activities of his soil conservation district in the building of upstream dams for flood prevention and as a means of lessening the need for downstream flood control. This is conservation of water.

He enjoys the wooded areas, the rugged terrain on which they exist, the tall trees that tower above the surrounding cropland, and the clear streams that flow through them. He works toward their preservation and improvement. He plants more and better trees, and he protects them against damage by animals and fire. This is conservation of forest lands.

He is interested in wild animals, birds, and fish, and he takes an active part in the development of feeding grounds and sanctuaries to ensure their presence in as great abundance and variety as local conditions permit. He encourages his children and those of his neighbors to study the habits of these creatures. And he does not abuse his hunting and fishing privileges. This is conservation of wildlife.

If this man is an industrialist, he insists that the property under his management be made to look as neat and attractive as the nature of his enterprise permits. If the property is situated within the city, he cleans up the grounds and paints the buildings. If it is located out in the open country, he beautifies the surroundings and develops an attractive recreation center for his employees and their families, building good will among them and their community. This is conservation of private enterprise.

If the processes in his factory evolve dust and smoke, he takes measures to ensure that these are reduced to as low levels as possible and prevents release of any toxic fumes whatever. He sees to it that all the effluent from his factory is put through a purification process before the water is released into a stream. He plans the surroundings to ensure sunshine and clean air for his employees. This is conservation of purity of the atmosphere.

If this man is an architect he seeks to do away with unsightly architecture, dilapidated buildings, automobile cemeteries, weeds in places where they don't belong, and slums, whether in city or country. He even cherishes the hope that the monstrous marble monuments in cemeteries will ultimately be replaced by small flat markers level with the surface of the soil. He wants these sacred grounds to be beautiful places where children can play and where retired adults will not be depressed. This is conservation of the human spirit.

If he is a highway engineer, he sees to it that all erodible cuts are covered with vines or shrubs or seeded down to grass. He thinks in terms of more than two winding strips of concrete that stretch from one great city to the next. He seeks for landscaped space, beautification of the right of way, and control of water runoff against possible damage to surrounding lands in times of heavy rains. This is conservation of public property.

If this man is a teacher, whether in the elementary school, the high school, the college, the university, the pulpit, or the theater, he bends his energies toward aiding child and man in his quest for knowledge and understanding. He endeavors first to know himself to the end that he can serve better in the uplift of those whom he teaches. This is conservation of the mind.

If he is engaged in research, he seeks to discover more about the universe, the world in which he lives, and all the other entities with which man is directly or indirectly concerned. He seeks to know more about the life around him, but he also seeks to know more about the physical and spiritual needs of man.

He might even consider research in terms of suitable means by which population growth can be kept under better control. This is conservation of man himself.

If soil conservation is this man's profession, his objective is "the promotion and advancement of the science and art of good land use and management to the end that conservation of soil and water and other related renewable natural resources—cultivated crops, grasslands, forests, livestock, fish, wildlife, and recreational areas—may be used and enjoyed by mankind forever." Such conservation is fundamental to the continued welfare of the nation.

Whatever the business or profession of any man, it is always possible to apply the principles of conservation to his line of endeavor. And there is abundant opportunity and great obligation for him to do something constructive in that direction. Conservation is not only a way of life, it is a way of thinking. And if enough people can be brought to a conservation way of thinking, this can be made and kept one of the most attractive countries in the world.

Some of the natural attractiveness of the landscape will have to be sacrificed with further increase in population. But in its place, usefulness with beauty can be added in new forms. The great expanses of corn, wheat, and cotton can be grown to greater perfection, the greatly improved grasses and clovers can come to be an ever greater joy to the eye and mind, the apple and peach orchards to the north and the orange and pecan groves to the south can be made more attractive and fruitful, the forests can be changed from the present indifferent species to the better and more productive types with systematic harvesting and replanting procedures, and wildlife can be further developed and better protected.

There can be many more beautiful public buildings, with spacious grounds. Parks can be enlarged and beautified. Private residences and the yards and gardens surrounding them can be made more attractive. And one must not forget the many fine breeds of livestock and the many smaller forms of animal life that can be raised to higher degrees of perfection. Finally, there are great possibilities for improvement in man himself arising out of a greater appreciation of our renewable natural resources.

The thing that numbs the heart is this
That man cannot devise
Some scheme of life to banish fear
That lurks in most men's eyes.
Fear of the lack of shelter, food
And fire for winter's cold
Fear of the children's lacking these,
This in a world so old.

—JAMES NORMAN HALL

Chapter Fourteen

LAND, FOOD, AND PEOPLE

IN the light of modern science, the capacity of Earth to meet the food needs of man is much greater than most people realize. Many millions of acres of presently unused land the world over could be brought into crop production. Massive soil-moving equipment could be used to clear off the briars and bushes, level rough lands, fill up gullies, dig ditches to drain wet lands, and build dams to store water for irrigation purposes. Many more millions of acres of arid land could be watered. Presently unneeded water in humid regions could be stored for later use during periods of drouth.

The productivity of most of the land that is now being farmed could be greatly increased. Better systems of soil and crop management could be put into operation. Much larger tonnages of lime and fertilizer, from virtually inexhaustible supplies, could be applied to remarkable effect. Much more efficient crop plants could be developed by breeding and selection. Much better protection could be provided against insect and disease attacks. And much more could be done toward the development of better machinery to use on the land.

Great improvements could probably be effected in rain-making operations. Pure water could be obtained in unlimited supply from the oceans that surround us when need for it for irrigation and other purposes makes this imperative. The plankton, as well as the fish, in the several seas could be utilized to a much greater degree. Algae could be grown in water culture on a large scale for food production. Much larger acreages of sugar crops could be grown and this sugar, together with urea and other fertilizers, could be fed to yeast with resulting production of high-protein foods. In case of need, forest growth could be transformed into food by the same procedure.

There is no longer any limit to the supply of energy that can be developed for use in the production of raw food materials and their manufacture into the finished products, as well as for meeting the power needs of all our other enterprises. Large quantities of coal, oil, and gas are at our disposal, as is the energy of falling water and of winds, waves, and tides. The rays of the desert sun can be concentrated to supply large amounts of energy. Still larger quantities of energy will soon be available as a result of developments in nuclear fission. And inexhaustible supplies of energy from nuclear fusion are in the offing. With abundant supplies of energy, hopefully at reasonably low production costs, there is virtually no limit to the possibilities of adding to the food supply.

Some scientists think that we shall be able in due time to synthesize sugar by factory procedures in much the same manner as it is now being done by sugar cane and sugar beets. If such a process could be made to operate on a factory belt-line basis, the possibilities would then exist for producing protein foods by microbial procedures on a large scale.

All of these developments will require time and great expense will be involved. As the late Charles F. Kettering of the General Motors Research Staff once said: "Anything you can think of today can be done, but it takes time. . . . With willing hands and open minds, the future will be greater than the most fantastic story you can write. You will always underrate it."

The element of time in relation to meeting the food needs of the people in overpopulated countries where widespread hunger now prevails presents a troublesome problem. Recently, an agricultural scientist in India made an exhaustive study of the possibilities for increasing agricultural production in his country. He proposed to divert much larger quantities of river water into irrigation channels, to greatly improve the heritage of the crops that are being grown, to develop much better systems of soil and crop management, and to make many more tons of fertilizer available for use over the next fifty years. The calculated gains in food production from these suggested improvements were very large.

But when this Indian scientist estimated the number of additional people that would have to be fed by the end of that period at present rates of population growth, he discovered that less food per person would be available then than now. To him, the only way out of this country's dilemma was to lower the birth rate. As a starting point he suggested that an effort be made to spread the concept that any woman who gave birth to more than three children was an improvident mother.

Present world population is estimated at nearly three billion people. This number is expected to be doubled by the end of this century, now less than forty years away. The annual rate of population increase the world over is about 1.6 per cent, and it operates on a compound interest basis. Some countries have considerably higher rates of population increase than this. Others, of which Ireland and France are two outstanding examples, have lower rates.

It will be recalled that Malthus, in 1798, said that the primary controls for population were war, famine, and pestilence. He also mentioned moral restraint, but he was of the opinion that very little dependence could be placed on it. During recent years remarkable strides have been made in sanitation and in disease prevention. At the moment war is being held in check throughout most of the world. Thus two of Malthus' population controls are not operating to anything like the degree they once did. This leaves famine, the third control, as the primary one, and it is in operation in a large way in some of the more densely populated countries. Millions of people go to bed hungry every night.

Meanwhile the United States and Canada are troubled by large surpluses of feed and food grains. And both of these large countries are far from having reached their full food-producing potentialities. Agricultural economists of the United States Department of Agriculture, writing in the 1958 Yearbook, said: "If we took 500 million acres of our best cropland and used it as intensively as the Japanese use their cropland, we could feed almost 2 billion people—assuming that these acres are as productive as the Japanese acres and that we consumed cropland products directly rather than as animal products."

This estimate of the federal economists includes a highly important principle—to feed grains to livestock and then to consume their meat and milk, as we do to a large degree in this country, is a wasteful practice in terms of food economy.

Over four-fifths of the energy values of grains are lost by feeding them to livestock, and a like percentage of their protein values is lost as well.

It is only in countries where food supplies are in excess of actual need that any such wasteful process as this can be permitted. And it is quite apparent that if the need ever arises, the people of the United States can shift quite quickly to a diet of much more grain, potatoes, and beans and much less meat and milk, even though a great deal of grumbling might be heard. It would be on this basis that the two billion people postulated could be fed on the produce of the acreage indicated.

Yet considerably more than 500 million acres of land could be made available for cropping in the United States if there were need for it. The total available cropland in the United States is now estimated at 465 million acres. But by clearing, draining, leveling, and irrigating more of our land with the facilities now at hand, this acreage could probably be increased to at least 700 million. Additional land could be brought into use in due time by adding to the water supply for irrigation and by reclaiming large areas from salt marshes and from the ocean along our shores.

Even then, and after all the other industrial and living needs for land have been met, there will still be around one billion acres of land that is too dry, too rocky, too rough, or too mountainous for developmental purposes except for pastures and forestry. A large part of this area is now being used for grazing cattle and sheep. These grasslands will continue to have great value in maintaining a reasonably large supply of meat for human consumption, even after our population has grown to be much larger than it now is.

Potentialities for increase in food production are great in many other parts of the world. The Amazon River Valley affords an excellent illustration. Possibilities for rice production in that vast valley are tremendous. Certainly one billion people could be fed from its rice and other agricultural produce once the valley had been developed for agricultural purposes.

But a great many people would have to be put to work clearing this tropical jungle, bringing its tremendous supplies of water under control, and making conditions favorable for living; a long period of time would be required to effect these improvements. By the time the valley had been fully developed for agriculture, industry, and commerce, the population would probably have grown so greatly and the rate of increase would have become so rapid that little of the rice that was being grown would be left for export.

This is what has been happening in the valley of the Nile during the last century and longer. This river flows through a desert, its water coming from the rains in tropical Africa much farther south in the Sudan. By building dams along the Nile, water has been stored for irrigating the desert, thus transforming it into some of the most fertile land on Earth. But after each successive water-storing dam has been built farther up the Nile, the number of people in the valley has soon increased to the point where all the extra food produced by the use of more water on more land was being consumed.

Even if there were large surpluses of rice in the Amazon and Nile river valleys, and if the surplus corn and wheat now being produced in the United States and Canada, together with this rice, were available for distribution to areas of deficiency, its transportation to such areas would not be feasible on any large scale, except for an occasional extreme emergency. To do this would require shipment from deep in the interiors of the countries of plenty to deep in the interiors of countries of scarcity, an expensive undertaking, the costs of which the countries in need could not pay.

The primary difficulty in countries of dense populations,

such as India and China, was that they were overrun by dense population long before science had come to their rescue. Conditions were highly favorable for human reproduction. Even though the death rate from the war, pestilence, and disease was high, growth in population continued. And, within recent years, the rate of growth has tended to increase. The problems now presented are not only those of meeting the immediate food needs of the people but of overcoming illiteracy, ignorance, superstition, inefficiency, and tradition on a grand scale.

As Joseph Priestly once said: "It is futile to expect a hungry and squalid population to be anything but violent and gross." Its problems cannot be solved in a hurry. The economics of their solution is troublesome indeed. Under the conditions that now exist in such countries, a democratic form of government may be too slow in its actions, unless a great deal of educational and financial assistance from the outside can be brought to bear on the situation.

Fortunately for the United States, growth in population and advancement of science have gone hand in hand. This nation has never known want. Yet some of the people in the United States have, from time to time and place to place, been poorly fed, even between wars when food supplies were in great surplus. It should be possible to remedy this situation. But even if the United States were able to distribute its food surpluses to the advantage of those in need of them, both at home and abroad, new surpluses would soon be developed. And this is quite likely still to apply at the end of the current century.

There will undoubtedly be times, however, when temporary shortages of food will develop. These may result from a variety of happenings, such as a recurrence of the extended periods of national drouth that have been experienced in the past, the latest one during the years 1932–37. Occasionally, we have summer seasons of excessive rain or of extreme heat or cold. Devastating attacks of insects and diseases sometimes occur. Large acreages of crops are often destroyed by wind and hail. Farmers may become discouraged by lack of adequate incentive to produce. And there is always danger of another world war.

It would seem desirable to prepare for the possibility of temporary shortages of food, such as might develop as a result of abnormalities in the weather, from war, or from other causes. This would require large-scale storage, particularly in areas that are far removed from the sources of supply. And such storage should be undertaken not as a means of getting rid of surplus food but to take advantage of the surplus while it is at hand. The preference would be to store the more concentrated high-protein animal products rather than the grains themselves, since much more food value could be stored in a given amount of space.

Grains stored in the areas where they are grown are too far removed from the points of greatest need, and their transportation to these locations might well be much too slow in time of disaster. The problem is one of being prepared for any emergency that may arise, Scarcity of food has a more demoralizing effect on people than that of any other product they might need or desire.

We cannot take it for granted, even with modern science at our command, that we shall always continue to have everything we desire in as great abundance as we might like or even as we have it now. Our population is now increasing at the rate of one every eleven seconds, which is more than five a minute, about 325 an hour, 8,000 a day, 56,000 a week, and three million a year. This is equivalent to a new city of 60,000 in every state in the Union each year. And here again population growth operates on a compound interest basis. At our present rate of increase in the number of people we should have over 200 million by 1875, more than 300 million by the year 2,000, and in excess of one billion people by the year 2100.

We have long been encouraging population growth in this country and we are still doing it. An editorial in the January 10, 1955, issue of *Time* magazine included the following comment:

> Very little is known about the subtle and important relationships between population growth and economics. But enough is known to discredit Malthus. Americans can take present population figures as a promise of more prosperity. Gone, for the first time in history, is the worry about whether a society can produce enough goods to take care of its people. The lingering worry is whether it will have enough people to consume the goods.

This, in effect, is an invitation for more immigration and faster reproduction. Many industrial leaders agree with this philosophy. Business in the United States is based on the assumption that we shall continue to experience a very rapid rate of growth in population. Such growth is accepted with enthusiasm. But there is great need to consider what this may ultimately involve.

Commenting on this matter in the *Harvard Business Review,* Joseph J. Spengler said:

> Shortages which are being brought to light by the course of demographic events in the United States will be greatly intensified by the progress of population and aggregate consumption in other parts of the world, since these new areas will be drawing increasingly on relatively limited sources of supply, major access to which has heretofore been enjoyed by Americans.
>
> Of even greater importance is the fact that continuation of population growth is likely to intensify various social and economic problems solution to which will be largely sought through state intervention. Should this come to pass, the economy would become less flexible and

the freedom of individuals to do as they choose would tend to be highly circumscribed.

As more and more people are crowded into a given area, friction tends increasingly to develop among them. More space is required for industries, cities, suburban developments, highways, and airports, resulting in much less freedom of movement by man. Such restrictions are being much more widely felt. Edward Teller, one of our atomic scientists, is quoted as having said: "I suspect that ultimately the population of the Earth will be limited not by any scarcity but rather by our ability to put up with each other."

The preservation of open space for recreational and related purposes is presenting an ever more troublesome problem. Public parks are being overrun with people who seek some release from the crowds of the more densely populated parts of the country. Alaska has great value to the people of the mainland states in terms of open space. Even when the time arrives that the oil, mineral, forest, and fishing resources of this large area are being developed on whatever scale they may permit, there will still be plenty of space remaining for those who like to rough it out in the open as our pioneer forefathers once did.

Our many million acres of desert, grassland, and forest are highly important in terms of open space. Greater efforts will no doubt be made in due time to the end that these arid, arctic, rough, and mountainous areas are more quickly accessible to those who seek such space for recuperating from the pressures of the people who are crowded about them.

There are those who feel that fears are unnecessarily aroused by what is considered to be undue insistence on the need to conserve our renewable natural resources—soil, water, grasslands, croplands, forests, wildlife, fish, and recreational areas—for improved use in perpetuity. For example, Thomas B.

Nolan, Director of the United States Geological Survey, recently wrote:

> I suppose there will always be a tendency to accept a concept of conservation that is based on exhaustion and that proposes restrictions in the use of resources simply because it is easy to project the present. But I cannot concur that such a concept can ever prevail since it ignores the fact that continual change rather than permanent stability is characteristic not only of the Earth but of its inhabitants. . . . We will resolve such problems well in advance of the doom we are often so prone to see.

There is an element of truth in this. The Malthusian principle need never become operative in the United States, at least to any such degree as it has operated and is operating in the Orient. Before this could have happened to us our intelligent leaders would probably have insisted on drastic action to increase food production or bring population growth under control, or both.

The food problem of the Orient might possibly be solved in due time. Even as matters now stand, food production in these hungry countries could be brought to much higher levels than now prevail. Taking the world as a whole Harrison S. Brown says: "If the food habits were to change sufficiently so that the people of the world were content to derive their main nourishment from the products of algae farms and yeast factories, a world population of 50 billion persons could eventually be supported comfortably from the point of view of nutritional requirements."

Such possibilities are much more easily talked about than realized. And long before any such population density had come to pass, the world would certainly have had some devastating wars growing out of local and national food shortages. These wars would undoubtedly have wiped out many millions of people.

The real question is not how many people can we feed. Instead, it is how many people do we want or how many people can we afford to have. Can we not have prosperity without such rapid rates of increase in population as now prevail over most of the world, with the associated fears and possibilities of war? And cannot the people of the world bring population growth under control in some acceptable way?

In view of the enormity of the problems of land, food, and people, it is imperative that studies to find out the facts should be continued on a large scale. Such studies could uncover the population happenings of the past, analyze those of the present, try to anticipate the future, and outline the alternative solutions to those who represent us in national and world affairs. Our hope lies in the development of better educated democracies the world over that, knowing the evidence, will develop constructive programs to meet the situations at hand and those that, otherwise, might develop.

SELECTED READINGS

CHAPTER 1

Kellogg, C. E. *The Soils That Support Us.* New York, The Macmillan Company, 1941.

Mohr, E. C. J., and F. A. Van Baren. *Tropical Soils.* New York, Interscience Publishers, 1954.

Stefferud, Alfred, ed. *Soil* (*Yearbook* of the United States Department of Agriculture, 1957) Washington, D. C.

Thorne, D. W., and H. B. Peterson. *Irrigated Soils.* New York, The Blakeston Company, 1954.

CHAPTER 2

Clarke, Frank Wigglesworth. *The Data of Geochemistry.* Bulletin 770, United States Geological Survey, Department of Interior, 1924.

Flint, Richard Foster. *Glacial and Pleistocene Geology.* New York, John Wiley and Sons, Inc., 1957.

Longwell, Chester R., Adolph Knopf, and Richard F. Flint. *Outlines of Physical Geology.* New York, John Wiley and Sons, Inc., 1934.

Shapley, Harlow. *Of Stars and Men.* Boston, Beacon Press, 1958.

CHAPTER 3

Allen, Agnes. *The Story of Archaeology.* New York, Philosophical Library, 1958.

Emmons, W. H., G. A. Thiel, C. R. Stauffer, and Ira S. Allison. *Geology, Principles and Processes.* New York, McGraw-Hill Book Company,Inc., 1955, 60–120.

Stamp, L. Dudley. *Land for Tomorrow.* Bloomington, Indiana University Press, 1952, 48–84.

White, Gilbert F. *The Future of Arid Lands.* Washington, D. C., American Association for the Advancement of Science, 1956.

CHAPTER 4

Emmons, Thiel, Stauffer, and Allison, *Geology, Principles and Processes,* 1–59.

Gregg, Donald C. *Principles of Chemistry.* Boston, Allyn and Bacon, Inc., 1958, 1–24.

Longwell, Chester R., Adolph Knopf, and Richard F. Flint. *Outlines of Physical Chemistry.* New York, John Wiley and Sons, Inc., 1934, 144–220.

Mason, Brian. *Principles of Geochemistry.* New York, John Wiley and Sons, Inc., 1958, 41–154.

CHAPTER 5

Bisset, K. A. *The Cytology and Life-History of Bacteria.* Baltimore, The Williams and Wilkins Company, 1955.

Christensen, Clyde M. *The Molds and Man.* Minneapolis, University of Minnesota Press, 1951.

Kevan, D. C. McE. *Soil Zoology.* New York, Academic Press, Inc., 1955, 44–54, 403–11.

Waksman, Selman A. *Soil Microbiology.* New York, John Wiley and Sons, Inc., 1952.

CHAPTER 6

Bolton, Joe. *The Wind and the Weather.* New York, Thomas Y. Crowell Publishing Company, 1957.

Hambridge, Gove, ed. *Climate and Man* (*Yearbook* of the United States Department of Agriculture, 1941). Washington, D. C.

Mason, *Principles of Geochemistry,* 199–238.

Mills, Clarence A. *Climate Makes the Man.* New York, Harper and Brothers, 1942.

CHAPTER 7

Graham, Jack B., and Meredith F. Burrill, eds. *Water for Industry.* Washington, D. C., American Association for the Advancement of Science, 1956.

Hargreaves, Mary Wilma. *Dry Farming in the Northern Great Plains.* Cambridge, Harvard University Press, 1957.

Stefferud, Alfred, ed. *Water* (*Yearbook* of the United States Department of Agriculture, 1955). Washington, D. C.

Weickman, Helmut, and Waldo Smith, eds. *Artificial Stimulation of Rain.* New York, Pergamon Press, 1957.

CHAPTER 8

Clarke, George L. *Elements of Ecology.* New York, John Wiley and Sons, Inc., 1954, 185–276.

Fuller, Henry J. *The Plant World.* New York, Henry Holt and Company, 1956, 191–207, 233–58.

Robbins, Wilfred W., T. Elliot Weier, and C. Ralph Stocking. *Botany, An Introduction to Plant Science.* New York, John Wiley and Sons, Inc., 1957, 202–18.

Thomas, Meirion, S. L. Ranson, and J. A. Richardson. *Plant Physiology.* New York, Philosophical Library, 1956, 357–427, 489–520.

CHAPTER 9

Bear, Firman E. *Soils and Fertilizers.* New York, John Wiley and Sons, Inc., 1953, 230–339.

Black, C. A. *Soil-Plant Relationships.* New York, John Wiley and Sons, Inc., 1957, 248–319.

Clarke, *The Data of Geochemistry,* 218–60.

Millar, E. C. *Soil Fertility.* New York John Wiley and Sons, Inc., 1955, 139–247.

CHAPTER 10

Bennett, M. K. *The World's Food.* New York, Harper and Brothers, 1954, 1–58.

Callison, Charles H., ed. *America's Natural Resources.* New York, The Ronald Press Company, 1957, 61–107.

Davis, Darrell Haug. *The Earth and Man.* New York, The Macmillan Company, 1948, 114–479.

Shaw, Earl B. *World Economic Geography.* New York, John Wiley and Sons, Inc., 1955, 133–477.

CHAPTER 11

Bogomoletz, Alexander A. *The Prolongation of Life.* New York, Buell, Sloan, and Pearce, Inc., 1946.

DeCastro, Josue. *The Geography of Hunger.* Boston, Little Brown and Company, 1952.

Gilbert, Frank A. *Mineral Nutrition and the Balance of Life.* Norman, University of Oklahoma Press, 1957.

Price, Weston A. *Nutrition and Physical Degeneration.* Los Angeles, The American Academy of Applied Science, 1950.

CHAPTER 12

Bennett, Hugh Hammond. *Elements of Soil Conservation.* New York, McGraw-Hill Book Company, Inc., 1955.

Carrier, Lyman. *The Beginnings of Agriculture in America.* New York, McGraw-Hill Book Company, Inc., 1923.

Faulkner, Edward H. *Plowman's Folly.* Norman, University of Oklahoma Press, 1943.

Stallings, J. H. *Soil Conservation.* Englewood Cliffs, New Jersey, Prentice-Hall, Inc., 1957.

CHAPTER 13

Bromfield, Louis. *Pleasant Valley.* New York, Harper and Brothers, 1945.

Fuller, *The Plant World.*

Lord, Russell and Kate. *Forever the Land.* New York, Harper and Brothers, 1950.

Ordway, Samuel H., Jr. *Prosperity Beyond Tomorrow.* New York, The Ronald Press Company, 1955, 51–118.

EARTH: *The Stuff of Life*

CHAPTER 14

Brown, Harrison. *The Challenge of Man's Future.* New York, The Viking Press, 1958.

Malthus, Thomas Robert. *An Essay on the Principle of Population.* London, J. Johnson, 1798.

Russell, E. John. *World Population and World Food Supplies.* London, George Allen and Unwin, Ltd., 1954.

Stefferud, Alfred, ed. *Power to Produce* (*Yearbook* of the United States Department of Agriculture, 1958, 10–18). Washington, D. C.

INDEX